The Open University

T357
Structural integrity:
designing against failure

BLOCK 1
STRESS ANALYSIS

PART 3: FAILURE MODES
PART 4: STRUCTURAL
MODELLING

This publication forms part of an Open University course T357 *Structural integrity: designing against failure*. Details of this and other Open University courses can be obtained from the Student Registration and Enquiry Service, The Open University, PO Box 197, Milton Keynes MK7 6BJ, United Kingdom: tel. +44 (0)845 300 60 90, email general-enquiries@open.ac.uk

Alternatively, you may visit the Open University website at http://www.open.ac.uk where you can learn more about the wide range of courses and packs offered at all levels by The Open University.

To purchase a selection of Open University course materials visit http://www.ouw.co.uk, or contact Open University Worldwide, Walton Hall, Milton Keynes MK7 6AA, United Kingdom for a brochure. tel. +44 (0)1908 858793; fax +44 (0)1908 858787; email ouw-customer-services@open.ac.uk

The Open University
Walton Hall, Milton Keynes
MK7 6AA

First published 2007. Second edition 2009.

Edited and designed by The Open University.

Typeset by SR Nova Pvt. Ltd, Bangalore, India.

Printed in the United Kingdom by Latimer Trend and Company Ltd, Plymouth.

ISBN 978 0 7492 5267 0

2.1

FSC
www.fsc.org
MIX
Paper from
responsible sources
FSC® C013436

The paper used in this publication contains pulp sourced from forests independently certified to the Forest Stewardship Council (FSC) principles and criteria. Chain of custody certification allows the pulp from these forests to be tracked to the end use (see www.fsc.org).

CONTENTS

PART 3
FAILURE MODES

CONTENTS

1 WHAT DO WE MEAN BY FAILURE?

If, for whatever reason, a component does not perform the function for which it was intended then we can say that it has 'failed'. 'Failure' can have a range of definitions, from something breaking into two or more bits to a television with a fuzzy picture. Here, we are concerned with identifying what constitutes failure for the purposes of performing a stress analysis: that is, the stress at which failure is likely to occur.

In Block 1 Part 2 (Section 5.1), I briefly reviewed the stress–strain behaviour of some typical structural materials. You will have seen that there are various ways of characterizing the mechanical properties of a material. For example, under uniaxial tension a hot-rolled mild steel might yield (begin to deform plastically) at around 300 MPa, but it can continue to sustain a load until it finally fractures (breaks apart) at around 450 MPa. So, for the purposes of engineering structural design, which is the failure stress? For the most part, engineering structural analysis assumes that the material behaviour is linear and elastic, so the yield stress marks 'failure' because it indicates the point beyond which an increasing elastic load cannot be sustained, and the component's shape will have changed permanently.

So is the yield stress of a material all we need to know? Well, not quite. For one thing, it is useful to understand material behaviour beyond the yield point, so that when a failed component is identified we can diagnose what might have happened. A knowledge of plastic behaviour is also important in optimizing the many manufacturing processes that use plastic deformation to shape metals, and in determining how stresses are generated in materials during those processes.

The way a component eventually breaks can also provide clues to the stress state that caused it to fail: the path a crack has followed, for instance, can show what stresses must have been acting on it. Also, although our analysis of stress and strain has so far considered engineering materials to be uniform and entirely free of defects, this isn't always the case. The presence of cracks or flaws in a material can lower the stress that a component can be expected to sustain; this is the subject of Block 2.

Of course, there are some components that are designed to fail, or at least to fail in a predefined, controlled manner. One example is the provision of 'crumple zones' on cars, which are designed to absorb energy during an impact (Figures 3.1a and b). This requires the right combination of component design and material properties to work correctly. Another example can be seen on plastic mouldings that are designed to be broken off at a central sprue (Figure 3.1c).

For the time being I am going to concentrate mainly on the 'phenomenology' of failure and fracture, paying special attention to the stress state associated with them. Later, in Block 2, we'll return to look in a little more detail at the 'micromechansims' underlying failure.

DVD

Testing materials to measure their strength is covered in the 'Testing of materials and structures' programme on the DVD.

A phenomenological approach is concerned with identifying and describing something without necessarily providing or looking for a detailed explanation of it.

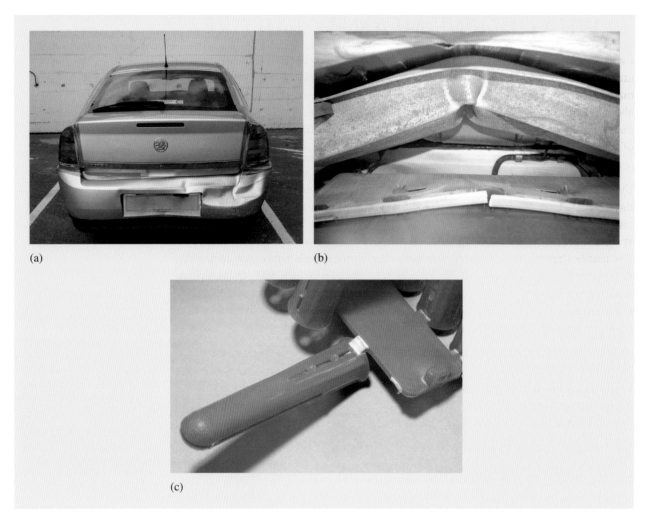

Figure 3.1 (a) External crumple zone on a car; (b) deformed rear bumper (viewed from beneath); (c) a plastic moulding showing a piece broken off the central sprue

2 FAILURE IN TENSION

I will start by considering materials that display brittle behaviour: that is, those that undergo little or no plastic flow before fracture intervenes. When stretched, these materials deform predominantly elastically prior to fracturing rapidly. The thing about elastic deformation is that it is *recoverable*: when the load is removed, the material springs back to its original shape. So, apart from the fracture itself, there is often very little damage evident in a component that has undergone brittle fracture; see Figure 3.2.

Typical stress–strain behaviour under uniaxial tension for a material failing in a brittle manner, cast iron in this case, is shown in Figure 3.3(a). The image of the fractured test-piece in Figure 3.3(b) indicates that the fracture surface has opened up on a plane at right angles to the direction of loading, across the cross section of the test specimen. The tensile strength of a brittle component is controlled largely by the presence of microscopic crack-like defects within or on the surface of the material. These defects tend to grow because they are pulled apart by a tensile stress; they do not grow easily under shear stress, and compression just causes them to close up. In general, brittle fractures occur at right angles to the direction of maximum tensile stress.

Figure 3.2   Smashed and reassembled ceramic mug; because the fractures are of a brittle nature the mug can be faithfully reconstructed

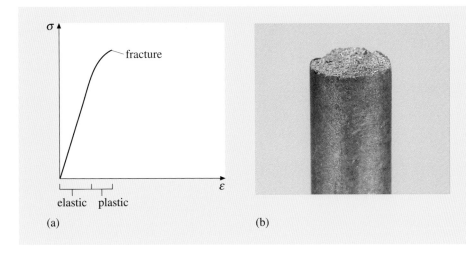

(a)   (b)

Figure 3.3   Brittle fracture in a cylindrical cast-iron specimen under uniaxial tension

EXERCISE 3.1

A brittle fracture occurred under the following stress state:

$$\begin{bmatrix} -14 & 8 & 20 \\ 8 & 185 & 12 \\ 20 & 12 & 40 \end{bmatrix} \text{MPa}$$

Suggest how the fracture surface would be oriented relative to the specimen's axes.

Now let's turn our attention to materials that behave in a ductile manner: that is, those that undergo significant plastic deformation before fracturing. Unlike elastic behaviour, the deformation associated with plasticity is largely non-recoverable; you can demonstrate this simply by bending a paperclip out of shape. During ductile failure the material literally 'flows apart' by plastic deformation; so, the fracture surface of a ductile failure is different from that associated with a brittle one and the deformation is driven by the applied stress state in an entirely different way.

To help understand this, it is useful to examine a specimen of material that has undergone extensive plastic deformation before eventually fracturing. Figure 3.4(a) shows the stress–strain behaviour of a ductile aluminium tensile test-piece. Note that fracture actually occurs a long way past the point at which the material might be considered to have 'failed' by yielding. Now, if deformation had been stopped just as the yield point was reached there would have been very little material permanent damage evident, and hence little clue as to what may be actually happening. Figure 3.4(b) shows that the specimen finally fractured on a plane oriented at an

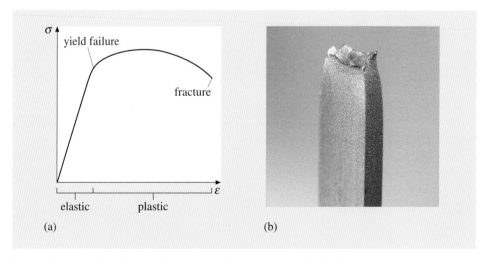

(a)   (b)

Figure 3.4   Ductile fracture in an aluminium test-piece loaded in tension

angle to the direction of tensile loading – about 45° in fact – very different from the flat 90° fracture seen for a brittle material. You can also see that the sample has become narrower near the fracture surface. This narrowing (or 'necking') and the orientation of the fracture are typical of many metal alloys that have undergone large-scale plastic deformation in uniaxial tension before rupture.

So what can we deduce from the fact that a ductile fracture is oriented in this way? Let's think again about the limiting stresses that arise during uniaxial loading.

EXERCISE 3.2

By constructing Mohr's stress circle for a uniaxial tensile loading of magnitude σ_t, determine the magnitude and direction of:

(a) the maximum tensile stress

(b) the maximum shear stress.

The answer to Exercise 3.2 indicates that under uniaxial tension the loading direction is, by definition, free of shear stress. Hence, the applied stress is also a principal stress. Recall also that the directions of maximum shear stress lie at angles of 45° to the principal stress directions, as confirmed by Exercise 3.2. In other words, ductile fracture occurs on a plane carrying the largest shear stress, not the largest tensile stress. This is because it is shear stress that drives plastic flow, not tension. Because there are two mutually perpendicular maximum shear-stress directions, there are two directions in which this flow can occur preferentially, as indicated in Figure 3.5. Eventually one direction predominates and fracture occurs. The 45° failure path associated with a ductile fracture is often called a 'shear lip'.

The region of 45° fracture associated with ductile failure can occupy any proportion of the fracture surface, depending on the material, the dimensions of the component and the conditions (e.g. temperature) prevailing during fracture. In fact, the entire fracture surface consists of a 45° shear lip only in components with narrow cross sections. When the cross section is thick and circular, a shear lip forms only around the circumference, giving rise to a 'cup-and-cone' fracture (Figure 3.6) in which one half consists of a flat-topped cone and the other half is a cup of complementary shape. The central flat part occurs because, as the specimen cross section reduces to a waist or neck, small cavities can form that cause the material literally to tear apart in this region. We will deal with the mechanisms underlying this type of ductile fracture more comprehensively in Block 2.

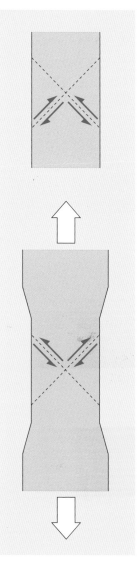

Figure 3.5 Ductile deformation leading to fracture in uniaxial tension

Figure 3.6   Cup-and-cone fracture in mild steel loaded in tension

Note that brittleness is not a materials property; it is the description of a particular fracture. In metals, whether a fracture is brittle or not can depend critically on the temperature at which the event takes place and the size of the part that fractures. It can also depend on the loading rate; plastics can be particularly sensitive to loading rate. Do not use the term 'a brittle material'; always say 'a brittle fracture'.

3 FAILURE IN COMPRESSION

Now let us consider the longitudinal compressive loading of a component with a constant cross section, as in a column or strut. This sets up a uniaxial compressive stress σ_c, which according to convention is regarded as negative. The Mohr's circle for compression is shown in Figure 3.7. It is similar to that for tension, except that the value of the applied stress is negative. Note that the maximum shear stress, equal to the radius of the circle, has a magnitude of $\sigma_c/2$, analogous to the situation in uniaxial tension. Indeed, ductile failure of most materials in uniaxial compression occurs at roughly the same yield stress as it does in uniaxial tension. Hence, for the purposes of engineering design, the failure of most structural materials can be considered to be the same in compression and in tension.

However, there are other aspects of uniaxial compressive deformation of which you should be aware. In compression the deformation of the component depends on its aspect ratio (length/width). If the aspect ratio is large (long and narrow), then the component has a tendency to bend and buckle, as shown in Figure 3.8 – we will analyse this fully in Block 1 Part 6. If the aspect ratio is small (short and stocky), then the component will not buckle. Instead, yield and subsequent ductile deformation will occur, reducing the aspect ratio further (Figure 3.9). This increases the cross-sectional area, thus reducing the stress on the component for the same applied load, making it more difficult to deform. Note that the opposite situation occurs in tension, where area reduction and necking cause an increase in

Engineers and architects commonly refer to a rod or member that is designed to resist longitudinal compression as a *strut*.

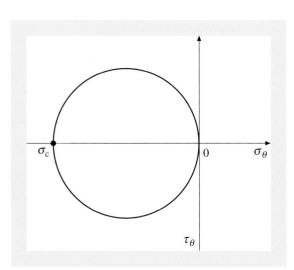

Figure 3.7 Mohr's circle for loading in uniaxial compression

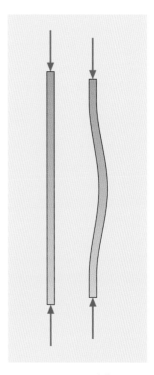

Figure 3.8 Buckling

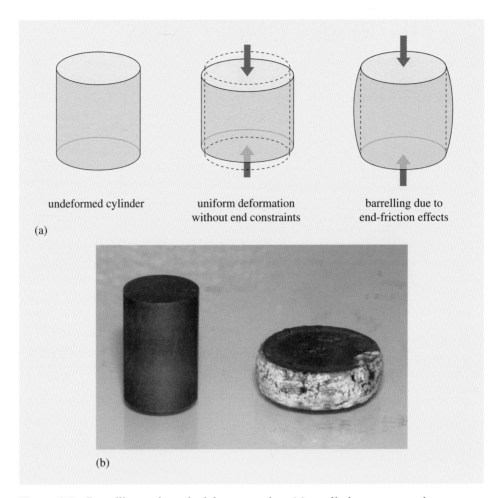

undeformed cylinder

uniform deformation
without end constraints

barrelling due to
end-friction effects

(a)

(b)

Figure 3.9   Barrelling under uniaxial compression: (a) a cylinder compressed
in the absence of 'end effects' would deform uniformly; in practice, due to friction
at its ends, it becomes barrel shaped; (b) titanium alloy specimen compressed at a high
temperature

the average stress on the cross section of the component. In compression there can
also be a tendency for the component to become barrel-shaped because of friction at
the loading points, which constrains the deformation. Furthermore, localized ductile
fractures tend not to occur except at very large strains. In other words, compressive
deformation tends to be more stable than tensile deformation.

Recall that brittle fractures starting from small flaws tend to occur at right angles to
the direction of maximum tensile stress. Because there is no tensile component in
uniaxial compression, brittle compressive fracture cannot occur in this way. Instead,
many structural metals that show brittle failures in tension actually show some
limited ductility in compression. Brittle fracture can occur, but usually only at very
large strains where the stress state has become non-uniform and is no longer purely
compressive; this can lead to tensile 'edge-cracking' in rolled or forged metals, for

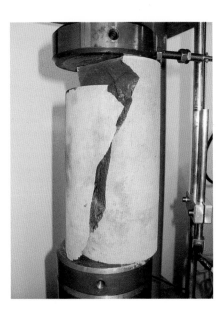

Figure 3.10 Shear fracture in a concrete column test-piece loaded in uniaxial compression

example. In columns of rock and concrete under large compressive loads, provided that buckling does not occur, many small internal cracks can form. These can interact to form a type of brittle shear fracture that is oriented at an angle of 20°–40° to the direction of uniaxial compressive loading (Figure 3.10).

4 FAILURE IN SHEAR

Although in practice it is quite difficult to load an object in pure shear, there are many cases in which this is achieved in an approximate way. For example, each link in a bicycle chain can be considered as a pair of single lap joints connected by a pin, as shown in Figure 3.11. If each metal connector in the chain carries a tensile load F, then a section through the shank of the pin at the interface of the connectors is subjected to shear stresses whose average magnitude is F/A, where A is the cross-sectional area of the pin.

Let's draw Mohr's stress circle for loading in pure shear with a shear stress of magnitude τ. Since this loading is one of *pure* shear, there is a set of coordinate axes along which only shear stresses act, and the direct stresses along these axes are zero. Therefore, the stress components along these axes are represented on the diagram by points with coordinates $(0, \tau)$ and $(0, -\tau)$. These points C and D define a diameter of Mohr's stress circle; see Figure 3.12.

Figure 3.11   Pinned lap joints in a bicycle chain

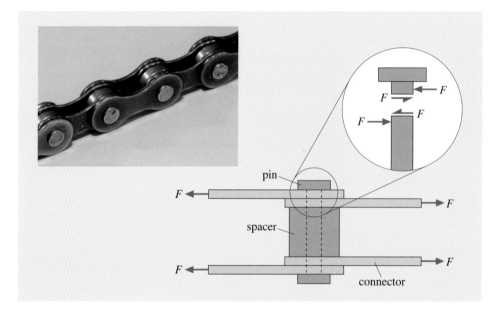

Figure 3.12   Mohr's circle for pure shear. Points C and D represent the maximum shear stresses

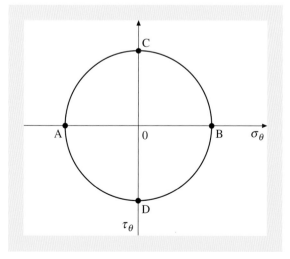

EXERCISE 3.3

What are the magnitudes and directions of the principal stresses for this state of pure shear?

SAQ 3.1 (Learning outcome 3.1)

Sketch one of the pinned lap joints shown in Figure 3.11 and mark on it the planes containing the principal stress directions and the plane in which you think a *ductile* fracture might occur.

If we assume that the shear stress is constant across the section of a pin in the plane of the lap joint, then there is a distinct possibility of a shear fracture across this section in a material that undergoes significant ductile deformation. Figure 3.13 shows an example of a ductile shear fracture in a composite pin. The direction of shear can often be inferred by the marks on the fracture surface and the presence of a small 'tongue' of material pointing in the direction of the shear. (Such shearing failure is most likely to occur in a joint where the pin is completely constrained by the plates such that the applied forces induce nearly pure shear; however, it is worth pointing out that, in practice, pins and bolts often undergo some bending inside the joint because of clearances, which can lead to the generation of a more complex mixed tensile and shear fracture.)

Figure 3.13   A pin, made of a metal-matrix composite, that has fractured in shear

5 FAILURE IN TORSION

Torsion is just a particular case of pure shear, but I have given it a separate heading because it crops up so often. I mentioned in Block 1 Part 1 (Section 3.3) that the material of a thin-walled tube, subjected to a torque about its longitudinal axis, experiences a uniform shear stress as shown in Figure 3.14.

I also pointed out that a circular solid shaft in torsion is subjected to a shear stress that varies from a maximum at the surface to zero at the centre (because the effect of an applied moment depends on the distance from the axis of rotation).

Let's consider, then, the outside of a tube or shaft loaded in torsion as sketched in Figure 3.15(a). The state of stress at point P is one of pure shear (Figure 3.15b) and can, therefore, be represented either in terms of principal stresses as in Figure 3.15(c) or in terms of shear stresses as in Figure 3.15(a). Note that here I am using an xy-coordinate system for the surface stresses in which the y-axis is always orientated at a tangent to the cylindrical surface; here we can say that the y-axis follows the 'hoop' direction around the cylinder.

Figure 3.14   Shear stresses in a tube under torsional loading

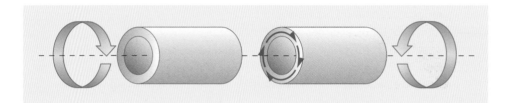

Figure 3.15   Shaft under torsional loading:
(a) applied torque T;
(b) Mohr's circle;
(c) principal stresses

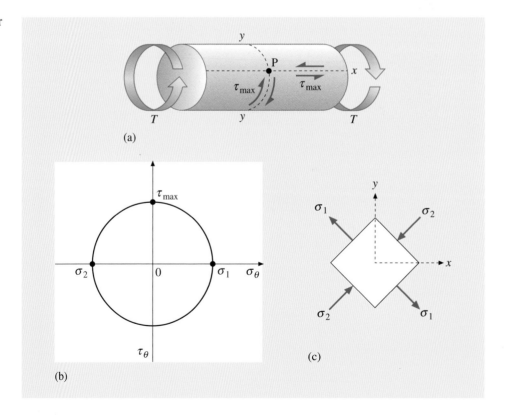

If the material behaves in a ductile manner, then it will fail by shear on planes of maximum shear stress: that is, on either a cross-sectional or on a longitudinal-radial plane (the dashed lines in Figure 3.15). This is confirmed by the fracture of ductile shafts, which usually break by shear on the cross-sectional plane; see Figure 3.16(a).

Brittle fractures usually occur on the plane of maximum tensile stress. In this case, such planes lie at 45° to both the longitudinal and circumferential directions. In order to maintain this orientation along the length of a shaft subject to torsion, brittle-fracture surfaces tend to have a helical shape, as shown in Figure 3.16(b). You can demonstrate this for yourself by breaking a stick of chalk in torsion – just grip each end with your fingers and twist (Figure 3.16c).

(a)

(b)

(c)

Figure 3.16   Overload fractures due to torsion: (a) ductile failure in an aluminium specimen; (b) brittle failure in a steel drive shaft; (c) brittle failure of chalk

6   FAILURE UNDER COMPLEX STRESS STATES

Of course, not all engineering structural components are subjected to simple stress states such as uniaxial tension or pure shear. The problem of designing a component to withstand anything other than the simplest of stress systems is that it is very difficult to determine, for example, whether or not yield will occur at any point in the material. The situation is exacerbated if the component is also complex geometrically. One way around this might be to design empirically, using past experience in the field, and build and test prototype components, measuring performance and deformations. This is often done in practice, but it can be very uneconomical in two ways: first, there are costs incurred in building and testing a prototype; second, there is a tendency for such a production item to be rather 'overengineered', i.e. conservatively understressed to prevent failure, and therefore wasteful in materials or manufacturing costs, or both. A 'properly' stressed item, i.e. one in which the stress state is accurately known, would be much more efficient, with savings in cost and weight.

To make life easier for the designer there have been various theories of yielding developed over the last 150 years or so. These have been formulated to relate the performance of material specimens in simple tension or compression tests to that of real components subject to complex stress. Some of these have proved to be useful and reliable; others are now out of date and even dangerous. I shall outline two of the theories that have proved most useful to engineers attempting to predict when yielding of a material will occur, using the yield stress obtained from a simple uniaxial test. For these theories the term 'failure' means yielding and plastic deformation.

6.1 Maximum shear stress theory (Tresca yield criterion)

The maximum shear stress theory simply assumes that yielding is dependent on the shear stress in the material reaching a critical value. As we have seen, the fact that many failures in uniaxial tensile testing occur at approximately 45° to the direction of loading (i.e. on the plane of maximum shear stress) implies that shear could indeed be the failure mode.

In Block 1 Part 2 (Section 5.1), when considering a two-dimensional plane element subjected to in-plane principal stresses σ_1 and σ_2, we noted that the maximum shear stress *in that plane* was equal to half the difference between σ_1 and σ_2. However, to analyse plastic yield properly for a general component that may be subject to multiple loads and stresses, we do need to consider stresses in all three dimensions. For the principal stress element in Figure 3.17, the maximum shear stress in *any* direction is half the difference between the maximum and minimum of *all three* principal stresses. Thus, since by definition $\sigma_1 > \sigma_2 > \sigma_3$, we can write:

$$\tau_{max} = \frac{\sigma_1 - \sigma_3}{2} \tag{3.1}$$

as the biggest difference in principal stress is between σ_1 and σ_3.

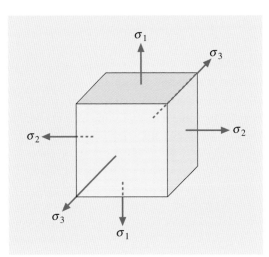

Figure 3.17   Principal stress element

The maximum shear stress τ_{max} at the point of yield in a uniaxial tensile test will be equal to half the uniaxial yield stress, i.e. $\sigma_{yield}/2$, so at yield Equation (3.1) becomes:

$$\frac{\sigma_{yield}}{2} = \frac{\sigma_1 - \sigma_3}{2}$$

which is used to define the maximum shear stress criterion:

$$\sigma_{yield} = \sigma_1 - \sigma_3 \tag{3.2}$$

In other words, under *any* stress state, yield failure will occur if the difference between the maximum and minimum principal stresses is equal to the measured uniaxial yield stress for the particular material. In fact, this remarkably simple yield criterion was the first theory of plasticity, devised as long ago as 1864 by Henri Tresca (Figure 3.18) while investigating compression and indentation of metals. For this reason it is widely known as the Tresca yield criterion and, despite its mathematical simplicity, it has been found to give reasonable predictions for engineering design purposes over the past 150 years.

Figure 3.18   Henri Edouard Tresca (1814–1885)

EXAMPLE

During the design of an engineering structure the principal stresses at a point within one of its members were determined to be −200 MPa, 100 MPa and 90 MPa. Could the member, made of an aluminium alloy (uniaxial yield stress = 250 MPa), sustain the calculated stress state without yielding?

SOLUTION

Using the convention $\sigma_1 > \sigma_2 > \sigma_3$ we have:

$\sigma_1 = 100$ MPa

$\sigma_2 = 90$ MPa

$\sigma_3 = -200$ MPa.

Thus:

$$\sigma_1 - \sigma_3 = 100 \text{ MPa} - \left(-200 \text{ MPa}\right)$$
$$= 300 \text{ MPa}$$

This is greater than the uniaxial yield stress of 250 MPa, and so failure would be expected to occur.

EXERCISE 3.4

A design for a rotating gas turbine disc is predicted to experience non-zero principal stresses at two different locations, as shown in Figure 3.19. The disc is to be manufactured from a titanium alloy with a yield stress of 860 MPa. Apply the Tresca criterion to determine whether the disc might be expected to yield at each of these two locations. Assume the plane stress condition applies to the disc so that the third principal stress in each case is zero.

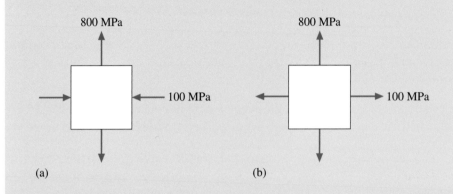

(a)   (b)

Figure 3.19   Principal stress states on elements at two locations in a turbine disc

Exercise 3.4 emphasizes that the Tresca yield criterion always applies to the three-dimensional stress state and, therefore, requires a knowledge of all three principal stresses – or at least enough information to decide which two of the three are the maximum and minimum principal stresses respectively. In plane stress, the zero-stress direction is not necessarily the 'minimum' stress, as there may be an *in-plane* compressive component, as in Figure 3.19(a).

The exercise also shows that yield behaviour is not easy to predict intuitively. You may have thought that the situation in Figure 3.19(b), with two in-plane tensile stresses applied, would be more likely to fail first, but that's not the case.

6.2 Shear strain energy theory (von Mises yield criterion)

The second popular theory of yield assumes that plastic flow depends on a function of the difference between *all* the principal stresses, not just the largest and the smallest. For yielding to occur, this theory states that:

$$\sigma_{\text{yield}} = \frac{1}{\sqrt{2}} \sqrt{\left(\sigma_1 - \sigma_2\right)^2 + \left(\sigma_2 - \sigma_3\right)^2 + \left(\sigma_1 - \sigma_3\right)^2} \tag{3.3}$$

where, again, σ_{yield} is the yield stress from a simple uniaxial test. Note that the incorporation of squared terms ensures that the result does not depend on the sign of the individual principal stresses. This formulation is based on a consideration that yield is related to the ☑ **strain energy** ☑ stored in a material when it undergoes shear deformation. The idea was originally proposed by Huber in 1904 and then subsequently modified by Hencky, Maxwell and von Mises (Figure 3.20). As a result, you may find that this yield criterion can be referred to by any of these names, although it is now most commonly known as the von Mises criterion in engineering circles.

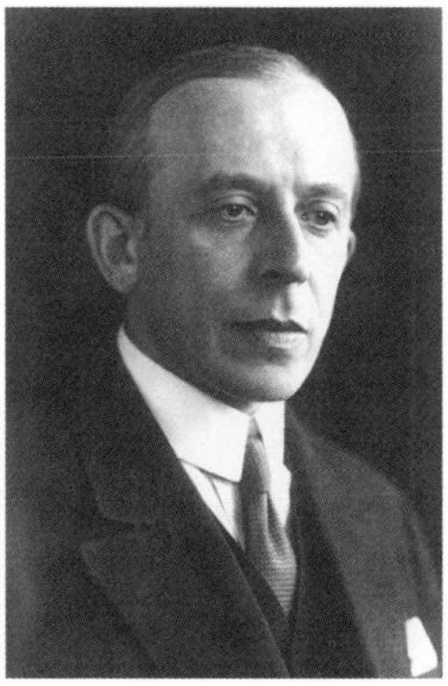

Figure 3.20 Richard Edler von Mises (1883–1953)

☑ Strain energy

We can get an idea of why a yield criterion based on strain energy contains a lot of squared stress terms by considering the force–extension curve for a bar deformed under uniaxial loading. Assuming that the limit of the material elastic behaviour occurs roughly at its yield point, the work done up to this point in stretching the bar through distance ΔL is:

$$\text{work} = \text{average force} \times \text{distance} = \frac{1}{2} F \Delta L$$

which is equal to the area under the force–extension curve up to the yield point, as shown in Figure 3.21. This work is converted to stored elastic energy in the stretched bar. If the bar has a cross-sectional area A and length L, then the energy stored per unit volume AL is:

$$\text{energy stored per unit volume} = \frac{1}{2}\frac{F}{A}\frac{\Delta L}{L} = \frac{1}{2}\sigma\varepsilon = \frac{1}{2}\frac{\sigma^2}{E}$$

with the term on the far right-hand side obtained by substituting for ε using $E = \sigma/\varepsilon$. In other words, the stored strain energy per unit volume at the yield point is proportional to σ^2.

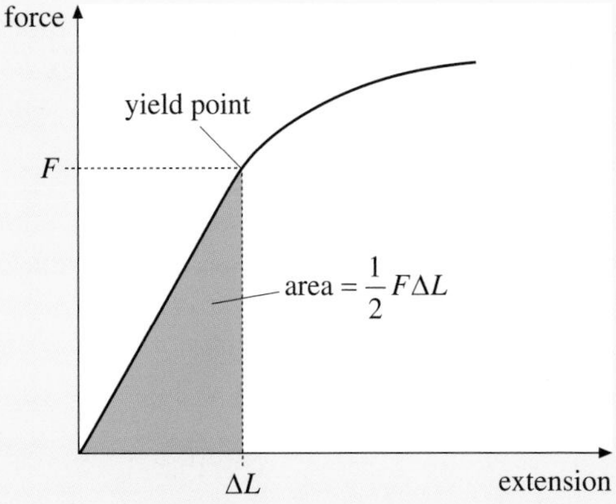

Figure 3.21 Idealized force versus extension curve for a stretched bar

SAQ 3.2 (Learning outcome 3.2)

Apply the von Mises criterion to determine whether yield will occur at the two locations in the turbine disc that you analysed, using Tresca's theory, in Exercise 3.4 (Figure 3.19). Compare your results with those of your previous analysis.

In the answer to SAQ 3.2, the von Mises theory predicts that failure does not occur for either stress state, which is a different result from when the Tresca criterion was used. In reality, the difference between the predictions of the two theories seldom causes problems, because engineers build significant safety factors into their calculations. The von Mises stress of 854 MPa of Figure 3.19(a) is sufficiently close to the stated yield strength of 860 MPa to cause worry.

In general, although the von Mises formulation is more complicated than the Tresca criterion, experiments indicate that it is more accurate. As your answers to Exercise 3.4 and SAQ 3.2 have indicated, the Tresca criterion tends to err on the conservative (i.e. early prediction of failure) side, which can lead to overengineering. This is not a bad thing from a safety point of view, but it is not cost-effective in terms of materials used, since, for a given safety factor, larger component cross sections need to be employed.

Despite being over 100 years old both theories are still commonly used by engineers, although the Tresca criterion has survived largely because of its mathematical simplicity. In modern times, the use of calculators and computers has led to the von Mises theory becoming increasingly more widespread. In particular, von Mises is frequently used to analyse complex stress states during finite element analyses. Results from finite element models are often quoted as 'von Mises stress', giving an indication as to how close to yield a component is, rather than outputting individual stress components and leaving it to someone else to do the calculation and make the assessment.

Finally, it is worth reiterating that these yield criteria are actually *empirical* relationships, formulated because they matched experimental observations. To this day there is no *theoretical* way of calculating the yield behaviour of a material subjected to a full three-dimensional stress field. However, as you will see later in Block 2, there is actually a good physical basis for incorporating shear stress into equations describing plastic flow. That's one of the reasons that the Tresca and von Mises criteria have stood the test of time.

SAQ 3.3 (Learning outcome 3.2)

After welding of an aluminium frame for part of a train body, the measured stresses at a point near the weld are:

$\sigma_x = 350$ MPa

$\sigma_y = 230$ MPa

$\sigma_z = 80$ MPa.

The alloy has a yield strength of 320 MPa.

Use the von Mises theory to confirm that yielding will not have occurred under this stress state. What is the safety factor?

7 DEALING WITH UNCERTAINTY IN STRESS ANALYSIS

Design engineers need to know up to what stress a particular material can safely be used. Is this just the yield stress? Unfortunately it is not quite that simple. The main problems are:

- Stress calculation – the predicted stress state is not known with a sufficient degree of accuracy for some reason.

- Stress raisers – some shapes result in local stresses much higher than the calculated average.

- Crack propagation – under certain conditions cracks or flaws in a material can propagate at stresses much lower than the yield stress.

It is worth looking at each of these factors in a little more detail, particularly the effect of stress raisers.

7.1 Stress calculation

The loads on a structure may not be known precisely. A good example of this is the effect of air movement. The forces exerted on high buildings and bridges by high winds can be very important, but the weather extremes over the life of the building cannot be predicted accurately. Certain structures can also be subjected to other unexpected loads, such as the impact of a lorry against a bridge or building (Figure 3.22). Oil rigs have to endure variable forces from wind, waves and tidal currents. Furthermore, in a complicated structure it may be difficult to determine how the loads are shared by the members; also, there can be forces arising from the effects of thermal expansion.

Recall that all the stress analysis we have undertaken in the course so far only really applies to materials that are *homogeneous* and *isotropic*. In reality, you should be

Figure 3.22   Collision of a lorry with a rail bridge

aware that all engineering materials display a certain amount of variability in their mechanical properties, which in turn can be influenced by changes in heat treatment and fabrication method. This is another source of uncertainty that may need to be taken into consideration.

In summary, the forces in the members can only be estimated; the theoretical calculations are only an approximation. However, you have already seen, during the freight-container case study in Block 1 Part 2, that the incorporation of a factor of safety into the stress calculations at the design stage can go a long way towards mitigating the risks associated with such uncertainties in the calculated stress.

7.2 Stress raisers

The effect of different features on raising or concentrating stress is shown in 'The Liberty ships' programme on the course DVD.

Certain component geometries result in local stress concentrations that are much higher than the calculated average; these are called stress raisers. A simple example of a stress raiser is a sudden change of cross section in a tensile member, as shown in Figure 3.23. The larger cross-sectional area is 200 mm², giving an average stress of $(20 \times 10^3 \text{ N})/(200 \times 10^{-6} \text{ m}^2) = 100$ MPa. The smaller cross section has half the area, so twice the average stress, giving 200 MPa. However, if such a member is actually tested it is found to fail at unexpectedly low loads. This occurs because at the narrow section the stress is not distributed uniformly, but is concentrated at the corners where the section changes.

In the case of a cut (Figure 3.24), the sharp edge can cause a very large increase in the local stress. Such stress raisers can be useful in everyday life: for example, glass-cutting is aided by scoring the surface of the glass, and the opening of drinks cans is facilitated by the thinning of the metal around the ring-pull; see Figure 3.25. In structural engineering, a stress raiser is usually a liability to be avoided. Hence, it is most desirable to transmit forces through smoothly varying cross sections, avoiding notches and sharp internal corners. Even a round hole in a member will act as a stress raiser (for example, a drilled hole for a bolt or rivet), so, where possible,

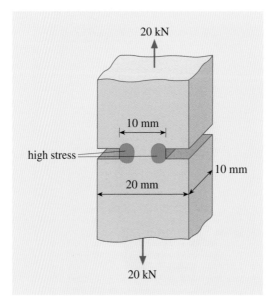

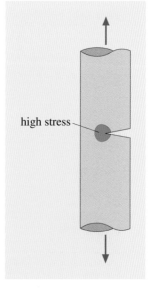

Figure 3.23 Sudden change of section

Figure 3.24 A sharp cut

these should be placed in regions of low average stress. Figure 3.26 shows the kinds of stress pattern that can arise at a circular change in section in a bar subject to uniaxial tension, as predicted by finite element analysis.

Figure 3.25   Stress concentrators assist us every day in breaking materials such as glass and chocolate, and in opening containers such as drinks cans and shampoo sachets

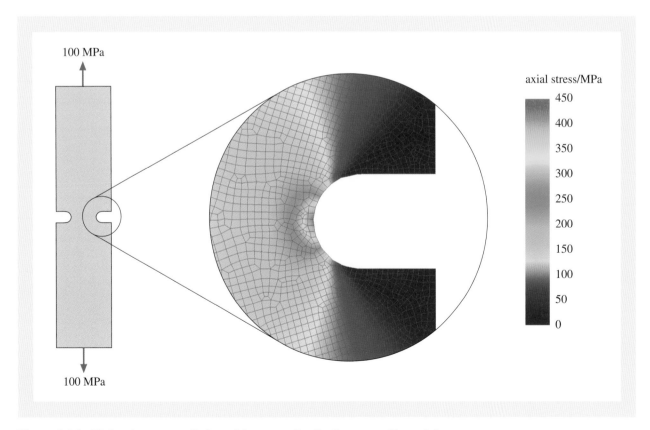

Figure 3.26   Finite element prediction of the stress distribution near a U-notch in a bar under uniaxial tension

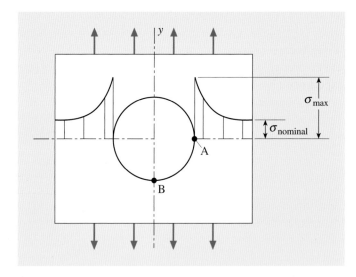

Figure 3.27 Stress distribution near a circular hole

In fact, design engineers aren't usually that interested in the overall stress distribution, just the value of the maximum stress. As a result, they tend to use something called a stress concentration factor K_t to summarize the effect of a stress raiser. This is the ratio of the maximum stress in the region of a stress raiser to the nominal stress expected to occur at the narrowest cross section:

$$K_t = \frac{\sigma_{max}}{\sigma_{nominal}} \qquad (3.4)$$

For example, theoretical analysis of a circular hole in a large, elastically deforming plate subject to a uniaxial tensile stress has determined that $K_t = 3$. In other words, the stress at the edge of the hole is three times higher than expected. The maximum stress occurs right next to the hole, at point A shown in Figure 3.27. (Such analysis also indicates that a compressive stress of equal magnitude to the applied tensile stress exists at point B, acting in a direction perpendicular to the loading direction.)

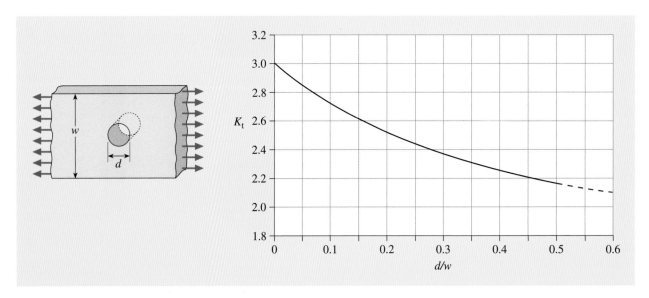

Figure 3.28 Stress concentration factors for a uniaxially loaded bar with a circular hole. Adapted from Pilkey, W.D. (1997), Peterson's Stress Concentration Factors (2nd edn), Wiley & Sons, Inc, p. 256; based on data of Howland (1929–30)

However, this theoretical analysis is actually only valid for an *infinite* plate. It turns out that similar calculations are impossible for real plates with holes, or for anything with a hole in it in fact. There are only very few simple geometries for which theoretical values of K_t can be derived. Instead, engineers rely on a large body of experimentally derived stress concentration factors, mainly determined using photoelastic models. Whole books of such stress concentration factors exist, covering all common geometrical section changes expected in engineering components; some common examples are presented in Figures 3.28–3.30. For instance, values of K_t for a long bar of width w containing a hole of diameter d are shown in Figure 3.28. Here, a value of $d/w = 0$ indicates a bar with width w that is infinitely large, i.e. an infinite plate, for which $K_t = 3$. The expected stress concentration factors for bars of finite width can be read off the graph, and these decrease with increasing relative hole diameter. Note that for the U-notch and shoulder-fillet geometries in Figure 3.29 and Figure 3.30 respectively, not all the ratios are plotted for cases where the stress concentration depends on more than one factor. In this case the graphs can only be a guide, and you might have to read from a 'worse case' than is actually true to ensure a conservative calculation.

A widely used sourcebook for engineers is *Peterson's stress concentration factors* by W.D. Pilkey, published by John Wiley and Sons.

Finally, I should point out that stress concentration effects usually lead to brittle-type failures. Stress concentration is often ignored in the design of components made from materials that are sure to deform in a ductile manner, provided that it is known that they will be statically loaded. This is because these materials can continue to sustain an increased load even after they have yielded, at least for a limited strain

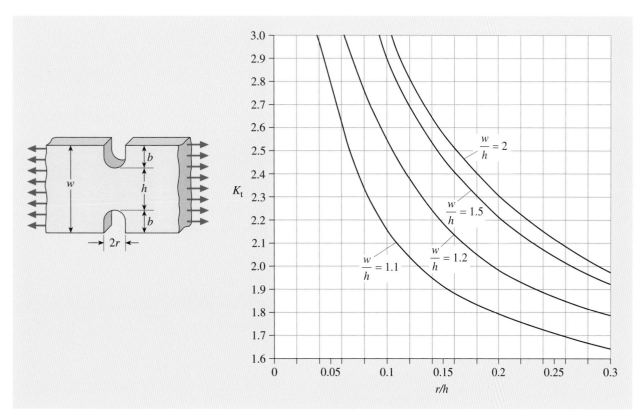

Figure 3.29   Stress concentration factors for a uniaxially loaded bar with U-notches. Adapted from Pilkey, W.D. (1997), p. 84; based on data of Flynn and Roll (1966); Appl and Koerner (1969)

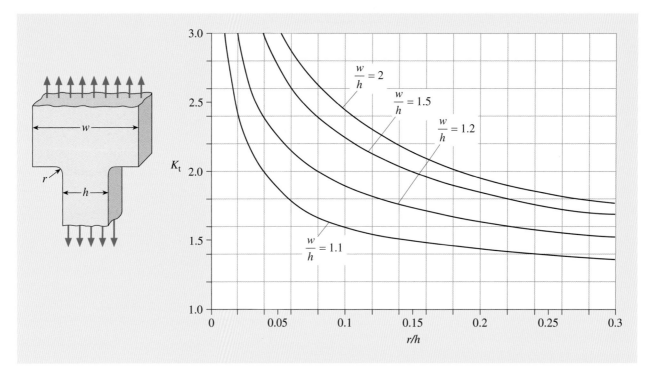

Figure 3.30   Stress concentration factors for a uniaxially loaded shoulder fillet. Adapted from Pilkey, W.D. (1997), p. 150; based on data of Frocht (1935); Appl and Koerner (1969); Wilson and White (1973)

(see Figure 3.4a), a phenomenon called *work hardening*. Hence, such materials already have a kind of 'built-in' safety factor to mitigate the effect of many stress concentrators. On the other hand, if there is any chance of brittle failure, then the correct assessment of the effect of stress concentration is highly important in engineering design.

EXAMPLE

A connecting plate 60 mm wide is made from 5 mm thickness steel plate (Figure 3.31). If a 12 mm diameter hole is drilled at the centre of the member, determine the maximum stress in the vicinity of the hole when a tensile load of 10 kN is applied.

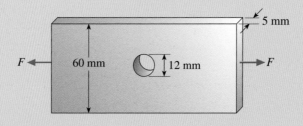

Figure 3.31   Steel member loaded in tension

SOLUTION

The hole acts as a stress concentrator, magnifying the expected nominal stress on the load-bearing area of the component.

When carrying out calculations with stress concentration factors, the nominal stress is always computed at the narrowest section of the member where the stress will be highest. Here, this occurs at the mid-section through the hole, where the area is:

$$A = (60 \times 5)\,\text{mm}^2 - (12 \times 5)\,\text{mm}^2 = 240\,\text{mm}^2 = 240 \times 10^{-6}\,\text{m}^2$$

and the nominal stress on this section is given by:

$$\sigma_{\text{nominal}} = \frac{F}{A} = \frac{10 \times 10^3\,\text{N}}{240 \times 10^{-6}\,\text{m}^2} = 42\,\text{MPa}$$

The stress concentration factor for the member can be determined from Figure 3.28. The hole diameter to plate width ratio is $d/w = 12/60 = 0.20$ and, reading from the graph, $K_t \approx 2.5$.

Finally, the maximum stress can be calculated by rearranging Equation (3.4):

$$\sigma_{\text{max}} = K_t \sigma_{\text{nominal}} = 2.5 \times 42\,\text{MPa} = 105\,\text{MPa}$$

EXERCISE 3.5

What is the effect on the maximum stress σ_{max} of *doubling* the hole diameter in the steel component of the last example (Figure 3.31), for the same applied load of 10 kN?

SAQ 3.4 (Learning outcome 3.3)

A turbine blade is fitted mechanically (it slots in) to a turbine disc: the two components are shown in Figure 3.32. The root of the blade has a series of grooves for locating it in the disc.

Assume that the blade can be modelled as a bar with U-notches as in Figure 3.29. The highest stress occurs in a section where the nominal width w is 40 mm, the height h is 30 mm, the thickness t is 15 mm, the notch depth b is 5 mm and the notch radius r is 3 mm.

The longitudinal force along the blade when the disc is spinning at full speed is 9.5 kN. From this, calculate the maximum stress at the root of the notch.

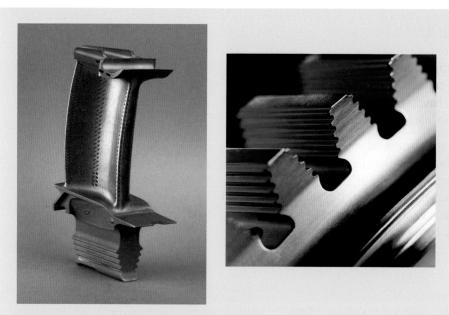

Figure 3.32   Turbine blade and turbine disc

SAQ 3.5 (Learning outcome 3.3)

A design for the end of a tie bar of rectangular cross section is sketched in
Figure 3.33. If the maximum allowable stress for the bar is 150 MPa, estimate
the maximum axial load that can be applied to the component.

*Hint: consider the bar to consist of two separate stress-concentrating features:
a hole and a pair of shoulder fillets.*

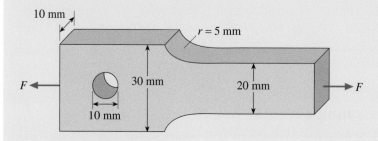

Figure 3.33   Tie-bar geometry

7.3 Crack propagation

The growth or *propagation* of cracks or sharp flaws in a material is a subject that we
shall deal with in detail during Block 2. Very few components are fabricated without
any flaws whatsoever, and most things will pick up surface scratches and abrasions
during use that can act as very small cracks. So it is worth drawing your attention
to the uncertainty that can be introduced into the estimation of failure stress in a
component when the possibility of crack growth at a stress far below the static failure
strength of the material exists.

A crack or surface scratch can be a most effective stress raiser. In fact, theoretical analysis of the stress concentration due to a sharp-edged scratch shows that it is extremely easy to generate stresses that are large enough to cause the flaw to grow. Fortunately, this doesn't always lead to failure, because the stress can be relaxed as the crack starts to advance. In materials that deform in a ductile manner, plastic flow can have a blunting effect on sharp cracks or scratches, which greatly reduces their stress concentration factor and so stops the crack growing further.

On the other hand, if the crack is large enough then it can propagate rapidly through a component, leaving it in two pieces. The critical crack size for which this happens depends upon the average stress and the mechanical properties of the material from which the component is made. A larger crack will propagate at a smaller average stress; so, a large structure such as a bridge or ship, which needs to be safe against a large crack, needs to be designed for a correspondingly low stress.

The bad news is that there are certain ways in which a crack can propagate even though it is smaller than the critical size for a particular material and stress. One example is *stress corrosion*, where the stressed metal is more prone to react chemically and is thereby weakened. Another is *fatigue*, where crack growth occurs slowly and progressively under a varying applied load. You will find out how to account for and design against all these aspects of crack growth in due course.

8   SUMMARY

In this part you have seen how the calculation of stresses you became familiar with in Parts 1 and 2 becomes important when linked to how a component may fail. The values and directions of all the principal stresses are important in determining whether a component is safely stressed or not.

You have also seen how stress can be concentrated quite significantly by features such as holes and notches, or something innocuous such as a gradual change in cross section. As has been noted, you will never be expected to know the stress concentration factors for particular geometries; but, if you ever engage with the design of something, you may well need to know where to look.

In the coming parts we will look at stress and strain in more complex structures, and some of the difficulties and simplifications used in modelling and in understanding real situations.

LEARNING OUTCOMES

After you have studied Block 1 Part 3 you should be able to do the following:

3.1 Understand the difference between brittle and ductile failure modes and their relationship with applied stress state.

3.2 Apply quantitative theories of ductile yielding (Tresca and von Mises) to assess the likelihood of failure in components and structures under simple and complex stress states.

3.3 Appreciate the role of uncertainty in stress analysis and be able to use stress concentration factors in the design and assessment of simple engineering members containing stress raisers.

ANSWERS TO EXERCISES

EXERCISE 3.1

The largest tensile stress component is σ_y, at 185 MPa. The fracture surface would be expected to be at right angles to this, so the fracture plane will be normal to the y-axis of the component.

EXERCISE 3.2

(a) For uniaxial tensile loading in the x-direction $\sigma_x = \sigma_t$, $\sigma_y = 0$ and $\tau_{xy} = 0$.

  The maximum tensile stress is clearly σ_t, and it acts in the direction of the applied load. This is illustrated by the Mohr's circle for this stress state (Figure 3.34), which shows σ_t lying on the normal stress axis with $\theta = 0°$.

(b) The maximum shear stress, as given by the radius of Mohr's circle, has a magnitude of $\sigma_t/2$ and acts at an angle of 45° to the applied load.

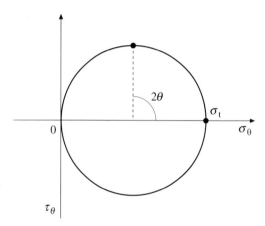

Figure 3.34   Mohr's circle for loading in uniaxial tension

EXERCISE 3.3

By definition, principal stresses are the normal stresses along those axes for which the shear stresses are zero. Therefore, the principal stresses are given by the points A and B on the horizontal diameter of Mohr's circle in Figure 3.12. The principal stresses act along directions inclined at 45° (i.e. half the angle between AB and CD) to the planes of maximum shear stress. They will have magnitudes of $\pm\tau_{max}$.

EXERCISE 3.4

(a) The disc is in plane stress, so one of the principal stresses, the intermediate one in this case, is zero. Hence:

  $\sigma_1 = 800$ MPa

  $\sigma_2 = 0$ MPa

  $\sigma_3 = -100$ MPa.

Using the Tresca criterion:

$$\sigma_1 - \sigma_3 = 800 \text{ MPa} - (-100 \text{ MPa}) = 900 \text{ MPa}$$

This is greater than the uniaxial yield stress of 860 MPa, and so failure would be expected to occur.

(b) In this case, using the convention $\sigma_1 > \sigma_2 > \sigma_3$, we have:

$$\sigma_1 = 800 \text{ MPa}$$

$$\sigma_2 = 100 \text{ MPa}$$

$$\sigma_3 = 0 \text{ MPa}.$$

i.e. the minimum principal stress is zero; hence:

$$\sigma_1 - \sigma_3 = 800 - 0 = 800 \text{ MPa}$$

This is less than the uniaxial yield stress of 860 MPa, so failure would not be expected to occur.

EXERCISE 3.5

The hole diameter is now 24 mm and the new load-bearing area is:

$$A = (60 \times 5) \text{ mm}^2 - (24 \times 5) \text{ mm}^2 = 180 \text{ mm}^2 = 180 \times 10^{-6} \text{ m}^2$$

with a nominal section stress of:

$$\sigma_{\text{nominal}} = \frac{F}{A} = \frac{10 \times 10^3 \text{ N}}{180 \times 10^{-6} \text{ m}^2} = 56 \text{ MPa}$$

From Figure 3.28, $d/w = 24/60 = 0.40$ corresponds to $K_t \approx 2.3$; hence:

$$\sigma_{\text{max}} = K_t \sigma_{\text{nominal}} = 2.3 \times 56 \text{ MPa} = 129 \text{ MPa}$$

ANSWERS TO SELF-ASSESSMENT QUESTIONS

SAQ 3.1

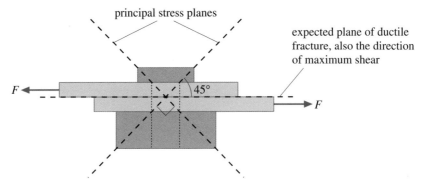

Figure 3.35   Principal stress directions and expected plane of ductile fracture for a pinned lap joint

SAQ 3.2

(a) Using the von Mises criterion with $\sigma_1 = 800$ MPa, $\sigma_2 = 0$ MPa and $\sigma_3 = -100$ MPa:

$$\sigma_{\text{yield}} = \frac{1}{\sqrt{2}}\sqrt{(\sigma_1 - \sigma_2)^2 + (\sigma_2 - \sigma_3)^2 + (\sigma_1 - \sigma_3)^2}$$

$$= \frac{1}{\sqrt{2}}\sqrt{(800)^2 + (100)^2 + (900)^2}\ \text{MPa}$$

$$= 854\ \text{MPa}$$

This is just less than the actual yield stress of the alloy and so the material is not predicted to fail. This is a different result to the Tresca criterion, which predicted failure for this case.

(b) For $\sigma_1 = 800$ MPa, $\sigma_2 = 100$ MPa and $\sigma_3 = 0$ MPa we have:

$$\sigma_{\text{yield}} = \frac{1}{\sqrt{2}}\sqrt{(\sigma_1 - \sigma_2)^2 + (\sigma_2 - \sigma_3)^2 + (\sigma_1 - \sigma_3)^2}$$

$$= \frac{1}{\sqrt{2}}\sqrt{(700)^2 + (100)^2 + (800)^2}\ \text{MPa}$$

$$= 755\ \text{MPa}$$

which again is less than the yield stress, and so the alloy won't fail.

This is the same result as predicted by using the Tresca criterion.

SAQ 3.3

Ranking the stresses in order, $\sigma_1 = 350$ MPa, $\sigma_2 = 230$ MPa, $\sigma_3 = 80$ MPa:

$$\sigma_{yield} = \frac{1}{\sqrt{2}} \sqrt{(\sigma_1 - \sigma_2)^2 + (\sigma_2 - \sigma_3)^2 + (\sigma_1 - \sigma_3)^2}$$

$$= \frac{1}{\sqrt{2}} \sqrt{(120)^2 + (150)^2 + (270)^2} \text{ MPa}$$

$$= 234 \text{ MPa}$$

which is below the yield strength, and so yield has not occurred.

The safety factor is $320/234 = 1.4$.

SAQ 3.4

The nominal stress is given by:

$$\frac{F}{ht} = \frac{9.5 \times 10^3 \text{ N}}{30 \times 10^{-3} \text{ m} \times 15 \times 10^{-3} \text{ m}} = 21 \text{ MPa}$$

From Figure 3.29, the stress concentration factor is a function of w/h and r/h. In this case w/h is $40/30 = 1.33$ and r/h is $3/30 = 0.1$.

Extrapolating between the lines for $w/h = 1.2$ and $w/h = 1.5$ for $w/h = 1.3$ gives a value for K_t of about 2.7.

So the stress is:

$$\sigma_{max} = K_t \sigma_{nominal} = 21 \text{ MPa} \times 2.7 = 57 \text{ MPa}$$

SAQ 3.5

We want to know the load associated with a maximum stress of 150 MPa for each feature.

For the hole:

Using Figure 3.28, $d/w = 0.33$; hence $K_t \approx 2.3$.

From Equation (3.4):

$$\sigma_{nominal} = \frac{\sigma_{max}}{K_t} = \frac{150 \text{ MPa}}{2.3} = 65 \text{ MPa}$$

The minimum section area at the hole is $(30 \times 10) \text{ mm}^2 - (10 \times 10) \text{ mm}^2 = 200 \text{ mm}^2$; hence, the associated force is:

$$F = A\sigma_{nominal} = 200 \times 10^{-6} \text{ m}^2 \times 65 \text{ MPa} = 13 \text{ kN}$$

For the shoulder fillets:

Using Figure 3.30, $w/h = 1.5$ and $r/h = 0.25$; hence, $K_t \approx 1.75$.

From Equation (3.4):

$$\sigma_{\text{nominal}} = \frac{\sigma_{\text{max}}}{K_t} = \frac{150 \text{ MPa}}{1.75} = 86 \text{ MPa}$$

The minimum section area is again 200 mm²; hence, associated force is:

$$F = A\sigma_{\text{nominal}} = 200 \times 10^{-6} \text{ m}^2 \times 86 \text{ MPa} = 17 \text{ kN}$$

Thus, the hole is the more 'dangerous' stress raiser and limits the load that can be applied to 13 kN.

ACKNOWLEDGEMENTS

Grateful acknowledgement is made to the following sources:

FIGURES

Figure 3.10: MeSy Me(Schlafes)Systeme GmbH, Bochum, Germany.

Figure 3.18: © V & A Images/Victoria and Albert Museum.

Figure 3.22: © Manchester Evening News.

Figure 3.32 (left): Reproduced with kind permission of the Department of Materials Science & Metallurgy, University of Cambridge and courtesy of Dr S Tin (now of Illinois Institute of Technology).
Figure 3.32 (right): Courtesy Rolls-Royce plc.

COURSE TEAM ACKNOWLEDGEMENTS

This part was prepared for the course team by Martin Rist.

CONTENTS

1 INTRODUCTION

In this part of the course I want you to start thinking a bit more about how we can use our knowledge of stress, strain and material properties to build mathematical models of engineering components and structures. Such models are vital in design and analysis, as otherwise all new designs would have to be approached empirically and/or heuristically and tested to destruction to ensure their safety.

In fact, you've already been carrying out simple structural modelling, particularly when applying the principle of equilibrium. Take the riveted plates we looked at in Part 1, redrawn in Figure 4.1. By considering the equilibrium of forces applied to the plates, it is possible to deduce the internal shear forces acting along planes across the rivet cross section. Knowing the dimensions of the rivet, we could then calculate the internal shear stress and, if necessary, make some estimate on the likelihood of failure. In other words, the principle of equilibrium allows us to build up a simple model of the riveted joint from which we can quantify the internal stress.

However, such a model is a simplification, as it incorporates certain assumptions: for example, we assume the rivet is a tight fit and that the plates are thin enough for the forces to act along a single line. That's not too much of a problem: any uncertainty we might have can be accounted for by incorporating a safety factor into the design considerations or, if it was really important (and we had the time and money), we could develop a more complete model that incorporated these complicating factors.

Now, the thing about a model based on equilibrium considerations is that, although it allows internal stresses to be deduced from external forces, it does not contain any information about material response – the elastic modulus, for example. In order to bring such factors into a model it is necessary to consider the strain associated with the internal stress. You have already seen (Part 2, Section 5) that constitutive equations are used to relate stress to strain. In order to use such relationships, the strains that develop in all parts of a deforming body must be *compatible*; that is, the strains must develop such that the material itself remains coherent, without holes or cracks appearing because of different strains in different regions.

Mathematical models based on strain compatibility bring information on the elastic or plastic response of a body; those based on force equilibrium do not. See ☑ **Metal-forming analysis** ☑ to get an idea of how these approaches provide different information, and how their application is sometimes restricted by the nature of the process or structure they are trying to simulate.

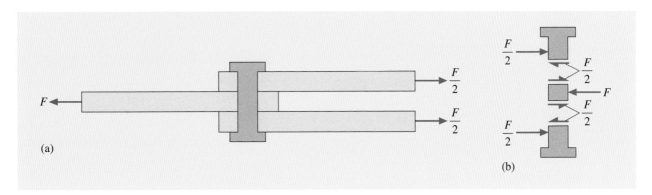

(a)

(b)

Figure 4.1   Three riveted plates in double shear

☑ Metal-forming analysis

Certain metal-forming processes, including forging, rolling and extrusion (Figure 4.2), involve bulk deformation of a workpiece with a small surface-to-volume ratio (hence the term 'bulk'). In all such processing a significant three-dimensional (triaxial) stress state is generated in the worked material, usually compressive in nature, which causes it to yield and then flow, leading to a change in thickness or cross section of the workpiece. It is important to know the magnitudes of the stresses that may arise during bulk metal forming, so that appropriate tooling may be designed and to ensure that the forming loads do not exceed the capabilities of the press or mill.

For modelling purposes, analysis of the triaxial stress states that arise during forming operations is often made easier by adopting a two-dimensional simplification (plane strain for rolling or extruding of sheets, or geometrical 'axisymmetry' for shapes that are symmetrical about an axis, as in closed-die forging). However, there are further complications associated with predicting tooling loads. First, significant frictional forces can arise between the forming die and the material that is being processed; these can vary with position along the die–workpiece interface. Second, not all the work that is expended by the press during forming is used to produce the desired shape: most of the work is turned into heat or produces 'redundant'

deformation that is not necessary to produce the final required shape.

It turns out that it is difficult to take account of both of these factors at the same time, so design engineers often take two simplified approaches for modelling purposes. These are based on a consideration of either the equilibrium of forces or the compatibility of strains associated with the deformation, and lead to either an underestimate or an overestimate of the actual forming load.

1   Equilibrium is most commonly used during forging or rolling simulations. If the internal forces that act on a workpiece during forming are identified – that is, the load necessary to make the material flow, along with any frictional forces – then, as they must be in equilibrium with the force that is necessary to produce the deformation, it is possible to estimate the forming load. This method, therefore, takes account of frictional forces, but it cannot include the influence of redundant work, because deformation can't be accounted for in the model. Hence, because the forming process will always require a bit more work put into it than the model predicts, such an approach always provides a lower bound to the actual forming load. The method is also very useful in assessing the effects of friction on a given forming process.

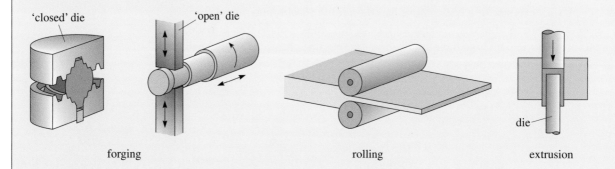

forging   rolling   extrusion

Figure 4.2   Bulk metal-forming processes: forging, rolling and extrusion

2   Strain compatibility can be applied to the modelling of extrusion processes. Since there is a continuous flow of material into and out of the process, and assuming there are no volume changes in the material during forming (that is, no cracks or fissures open up), the change in shape is accompanied by quantifiable changes in flow direction and velocity. Because such a model takes account of the deformation flow paths, it can include the effects of redundant work and, provided that the correct shape change is predicted, it will always give an overestimate, or upper bound, to the forming load. A lot of effort goes into minimizing upper-bound solutions to obtain better estimates of forming loads.

For most design or operational purposes it is more important to know the upper-bound solution, since this will ensure that the calculated load is sufficient to complete the forming operation. The accuracy of the lower-bound solution is dependent on the efficiency of the actual forming process – that is, on how much energy is wasted. Processes where the material flow is relatively simple, such as open-die forging or rolling, have little redundant work and hence have high efficiencies. Under these conditions lower-bound models based on equilibrium considerations can produce useful estimates of forming loads. However, processes such as extrusion and closed-die forging involve significant amounts of redundant work and are most usefully modelled using upper-bound theory, based on compatibility considerations.

In Part 4, I want to use some other, diverse examples to explore how the considerations of equilibrium and compatibility can provide a basis for mathematical models of engineering materials and structures.

2 EXAMPLE 1: MODELLING STRUCTURAL COMPOSITES

In this first example, I will consider the question of how to model *composite* materials, i.e. those having an internal structure that consists of two or more distinct material components. Up until now, our analysis has focused on the stress and deformation behaviour of structures composed of just one sort of material, usually a metal. Most of the materials we have looked at have been both homogeneous and isotropic: that is, with the same uniform mechanical properties in all directions. Composites, on the other hand, may be inhomogeneous and anisotropic: that is, with material properties that are highly directional. They often take the form of a matrix material that contains discrete components of one or more other materials. These components can be particles, fibres, sheets or, in the case of foams, voids containing gas or even liquid; some examples are presented in Figure 4.3.

Many composites available today for load-bearing applications use polymers as the matrix material, mainly because these are easily processed and form low-density, lightweight products. A familiar example is fibreglass, in which glass fibres are mixed with a polymeric resin; and many plastic mouldings comprise ceramic

Figure 4.3 Various composite structural materials: (a) a glass-fibre and polyester composite, 'fibreglass'; (b) an aluminium–silicon carbide metal-matrix composite; (c) plywood; (d) concrete; (e) metallic copper foam

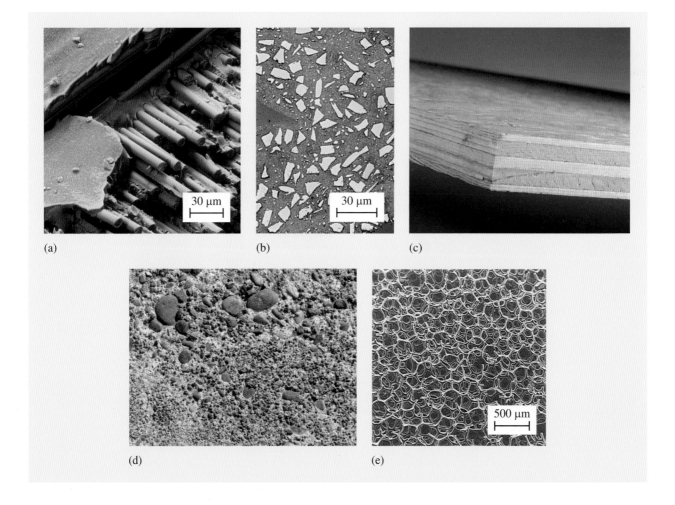

(a)   30 μm

(b)   30 μm

(c)

(d)

(e)   500 μm

particles embedded in a polyurethane matrix. Metal composites include titanium alloys reinforced with silicon carbide (SiC) ceramic fibres, used for aerospace applications, and aluminium alloys containing wear-resistant SiC particles, found in vehicle brake discs. Common construction materials, such as concrete and wood, are also composites. Concrete is a composite of sand and a coarse aggregate, bonded with a cement matrix; and wood is a naturally occurring fibre-reinforced composite of polymer cells embedded in a different polymer matrix. Composites based on cladding are also made, for example, by sandwiching fibreglass between two layers of aluminium or plastic sheet.

Modelling composites is a good way of appreciating how more complex, multicomponent structures can be analysed. Provided the composite is made of solid materials that are not too dissimilar to each other, and that are bonded strongly together, it is possible to carry out some straightforward analysis based on the principles of equilibrium and compatibility.

Here I'll consider two of the simplest models for describing the stresses and strains in such materials. They consider the composite as being equivalent to a combination of elementary blocks of the component materials, but differ in their assumptions as to how these blocks are arranged in relation to the direction of the applied stress.

2.1 Homogeneous strain model

In the first model, known as the *homogeneous strain* or *isostrain* model, it is assumed that the components from which the composite is made are aligned parallel with each other, and with the direction of loading, as shown in Figure 4.4 for a two-component composite (that is, a composite made up from two different

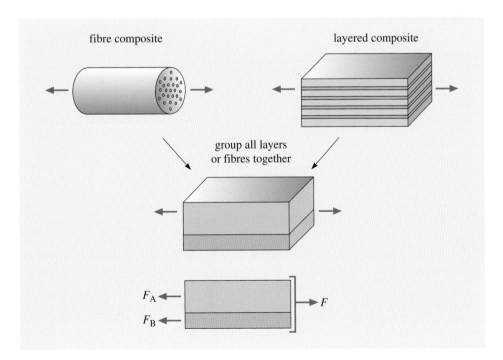

Figure 4.4   Homogeneous strain model for a two-component composite material

types of material). In this simple model it is the total load-bearing cross-sectional areas of the components that is important, rather than their shape or distribution, hence all the layers or fibres of each component can be grouped together to form two blocks.

By considering the equilibrium of the horizontal forces in the two-block model of Figure 4.4, the total load F on the composite must be the sum of the loads F_A and F_B on the individual blocks:

$$F = F_A + F_B$$

These forces lead to stresses that can be quantified by substituting for the total force using $F = \sigma A$, and for the component forces using $F_A = \sigma_A A_A$ and $F_B = \sigma_B A_B$, giving:

$$A\sigma = A_A \sigma_A + A_B \sigma_B$$

$$\sigma = \frac{A_A}{A}\sigma_A + \frac{A_B}{A}\sigma_B$$

which can be rewritten as:

$$\sigma = \left(A_f\right)_A \sigma_A + \left(A_f\right)_B \sigma_B \tag{4.1}$$

where $\left(A_f\right)_A = A_A/A$ and $\left(A_f\right)_B = A_B/A$ are the *area fractions* of the respective components.

If perfect bonding is assumed between the components, then there is strain compatibility and the length of the two materials remains the same. This means that the area fraction of each component must be the same as its volume fraction; for example, for component A, length L:

$$\frac{A_A}{A} = \frac{A_A L}{AL} = \frac{V_A}{V}$$

And hence Equation (4.1) can also be written as:

$$\sigma = \left(V_f\right)_A \sigma_A + \left(V_f\right)_B \sigma_B \tag{4.2}$$

where $\left(V_f\right)_A = V_A/V$ and $\left(V_f\right)_B = V_B/V$ are the component *volume fractions*. Since the total volume fraction of the composite is equal to unity, then clearly $\left(V_f\right)_A + \left(V_f\right)_B = 1$.

One of the key aspects in composite design is the stiffness of the overall material. Quite often the reason for using a composite is that its stiffness-to-weight ratio is much higher than that of the unreinforced material. The stiffness can be incorporated into the model by assuming linear-elastic behaviour and using Hooke's law, $E = \sigma/\varepsilon$, to substitute for stress in Equation (4.2):

$$E\varepsilon = \left(V_f\right)_A E_A \varepsilon_A + \left(V_f\right)_B E_B \varepsilon_B$$

and again applying the strain compatibility condition, $\varepsilon = \varepsilon_A = \varepsilon_B$, this simply reduces to:

$$E = \left(V_f\right)_A E_A + \left(V_f\right)_B E_B \qquad (4.3)$$

So the composite modulus is obtained by adding the individual elastic moduli of the component phases in the fractions that they are present in the composite. Note that there is also the question of strain compatibility *perpendicular* to the loading direction, because of the Poisson effect. In fact, this is not a problem if the two component materials have the same Poisson's ratio, because then the lateral strain in each is the same and the isostrain model still provides an exact solution to the problem. If the Poisson's ratios are different, then stresses at the interfaces between the two components can arise. However, most materials have Poisson's ratios in the fairly narrow range of about 0.2–0.3, and it turns out that the deviations from the model are very small in practice.

EXERCISE 4.1

A glass-fibre–epoxy composite contains 65% by volume of aligned glass fibres ($E_g = 72$ GPa) in an epoxy resin matrix ($E_e = 3.5$ GPa).

What is the modulus of the composite parallel to the axis of the fibres?

The homogeneous strain model derived above is also known as the *law* (or *rule*) *of mixtures* and is frequently invoked to represent a whole range of composite properties, including density and electrical or thermal conductivity, as well as stress and elastic modulus. It is also sometimes referred to as the *Voigt model* after Woldemar Voigt (Figure 4.5), a German physicist, who originally developed it in 1889 for the modulus of polycrystalline metals.

Figure 4.5 Woldemar Voigt (1850–1919)

SAQ 4.1 (Learning outcome 4.2)

(a) A large concrete support column has a square cross section of 0.25 m² and is reinforced internally by 10 steel bars each of cross section 500 mm². If the elastic modulus of the concrete is $E_c = 50$ GPa and that of the steel is $E_s = 200$ GPa, determine the elastic modulus of the composite column assuming a homogeneous strain model.

Hint: concrete is itself a composite, but by considering its overall modulus, we can treat it as a uniform matrix in this case.

(b) If the column supports a compressive load of 2000 kN, calculate the longitudinal strain in the column by applying Hooke's law to the column as a whole.

(c) For the same load, determine the average stress in the concrete and in the steel by applying Hooke's law to each component, again assuming strain compatibility.

(d) Finally, confirm the stress is partitioned between the steel and concrete according to Equation (4.1).

2.2 Homogeneous stress model

In the second model, the *homogeneous stress* or *isostress* model, the composite is idealized as blocks of equal cross-sectional area but different length arranged in series, as shown in Figure 4.6. This model is a good approximation for a fibre composite loaded at right angles to the fibre direction, where there is only one continuous component (the matrix), or a laminated composite that has no continuous components. In both these cases, a series model is a better description of the interaction between the components than a parallel model. Here, horizontal equilibrium dictates that each component is subjected to the same force, equal to the overall force applied to the composite. The stress across each block, therefore, is also the same, but the strains are different.

For the isostress model, the total extension of the composite ΔL is given by the sum of the individual extensions:

$$\Delta L = \Delta L_A + \Delta L_B$$

Now, using $\Delta L = \varepsilon L$ and $\varepsilon = \sigma / E$ for the composite as a whole, and similar expressions for the two components, we get:

$$\varepsilon L = \varepsilon_A L_A + \varepsilon_B L_B$$

$$\frac{\sigma L}{E} = \frac{\sigma_A L_A}{E_A} + \frac{\sigma_B L_B}{E_B}$$

Figure 4.6 Homogeneous stress model for a two-component composite material

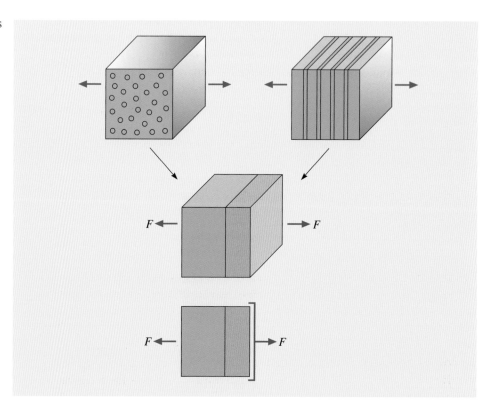

and since $\sigma = \sigma_A = \sigma_B$ this reduces to:

$$\frac{1}{E} = \frac{L_A}{L}\frac{1}{E_A} + \frac{L_B}{L}\frac{1}{E_B} \tag{4.4}$$

where L_A/L and L_B/L are the length fractions of the two components. Based on a similar argument to that used previously for the area fractions, the length fractions in this model are equal to the volume fractions, $(V_f)_A$ and $(V_f)_B$; for example, for component A, area A:

$$\frac{L_A}{L} = \frac{AL_A}{AL} = \frac{V_A}{V}$$

So, Equation (4.4) can be written as:

$$\frac{1}{E} = \frac{(V_f)_A}{E_A} + \frac{(V_f)_B}{E_B} \tag{4.5}$$

In a similar way to the Voigt model, the homogeneous stress model is often named after *Reuss*, who came up with an alternative way of modelling polycrystalline elasticity, after Voigt, in 1929.

EXERCISE 4.2

In Exercise 4.1 you calculated the modulus of a glass-fibre–epoxy composite parallel to the fibre direction $\left((V_f)_g = 0.65,\ E_g = 72\ \text{GPa},\ E_e = 3.5\ \text{GPa}\right)$. The result of that theoretical calculation is presented in Table 4.1 along with measured values of the modulus, parallel and perpendicular to the fibre direction, derived from tensile tests on composite specimens.

Complete the table by calculating the theoretical modulus perpendicular to the fibres using the homogeneous stress model.

Table 4.1   Moduli of a glass–epoxy composite

Modulus	Calculated/GPa	Measured/GPa
$E_\parallel$ (parallel to fibres)	48.0	46.5
$E_\perp$ (perpendicular to fibres)		16.4

Comparison of the theoretical and measured values of elastic modulus for the glass–epoxy composite in your completed table is interesting. The calculated values are quite close to the measured values, but somewhat higher for loading parallel to the fibres and lower for loading perpendicular to the fibres. This makes sense if you consider that the two models are idealizations of the composite material; because the fibres can never be perfectly aligned in one direction, our models represent two extremes of reality – the truth lies somewhere in between.

SAQ 4.2 (Learning outcomes 4.1 and 4.2)

Stainless-steel-clad aluminium is a modern composite manufactured by rolling a sandwich of aluminium between two sheets of stainless steel (Figure 4.7), followed by heat treatment to promote bonding between the layers. Relatively pure (unalloyed) aluminium must be used to ensure that the bond is strong. This lightweight metal composite combines the excellent electrical and thermal conductivity of aluminium with the corrosion and abrasion resistance of stainless steel, and is used in cooking utensils, car and aircraft parts, and for certain structural applications where attractiveness is important (shop fascias, for example).

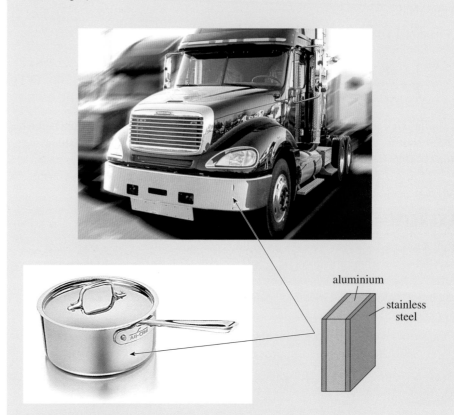

Figure 4.7   Stainless-steel-clad aluminium

(a) A particular stainless-steel-clad aluminium sandwich sheet is 2 mm thick in total, with two 0.3 mm thick outer steel layers. If the elastic moduli for aluminium and stainless steel are $E_{Al} = 70$ GPa and $E_{ss} = 190$ GPa respectively, what is the modulus of the composite parallel and perpendicular to the plane of the layers?

(b) The thermal conductivity k of a material is a measure of how well it can conduct heat. For aluminium it has a value of $k_{Al} = 210$ W m^{-1} °C^{-1}, and for stainless steel it is $k_{ss} = 15$ W m^{-1} °C^{-1}, so aluminium is 14 times better at conducting heat than stainless steel. Assuming that Equations (4.3) and (4.5) can be applied to conductivity in the same way that they can to elastic modulus, determine the thermal conductivity of the composite perpendicular and parallel to the layers.

(c) When this cladding is used for structural purposes, the design specification stipulates that, under tensile loading perpendicular to the composite cross section (parallel to the composite layers), the average stress in the aluminium layer should not exceed 50 MPa. Determine the corresponding average stress in the stainless-steel cladding.

It is worth looking in a little more detail at the differences between the isostress and isostrain models. In Figure 4.8 I have plotted out the model Equations (4.3) and (4.5) for two different material combinations. These are curves of composite modulus versus volume fraction of component B. In the upper pair of curves I have arbitrarily taken $E_A = 35$ GPa and $E_B = 70$ GPa, so that $E_B = 2E_A$, and in the lower pair I have chosen E_A and E_B to correspond to those of polypropylene and glass (around 1 GPa and 70 GPa respectively).

The first thing to notice about Figure 4.8 is that the dashed lines, which correspond to the homogeneous strain solutions, give higher values of the modulus than the homogeneous stress solution for all values of volume fraction other than zero or one. In fact, the isostrain model provides an *upper bound* to all models of composite behaviour. In the same way, the isostress model provides a *lower bound*. This is consistent with the results in Table 4.1.

The second feature to note from Figure 4.8 is that the difference between the two models increases with increasing difference between the modulus of the two

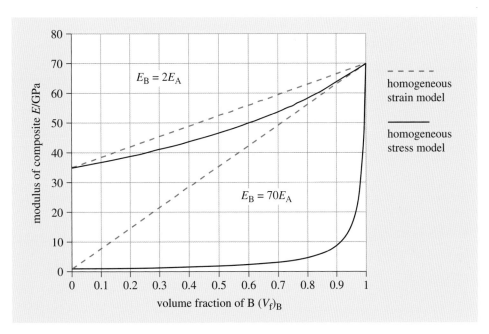

Figure 4.8   Composite modulus versus volume fraction from the homogeneous strain (dashed lines) and homogeneous stress (solid lines) models for two different values of E_B/E_A

components. For the upper set of curves, where $E_B = 2E_A$, the models differ only by a maximum of about 10% in predicted composite modulus. When $E_B = 70E_A$, on the other hand, their greatest difference is by a factor of almost 20. Further, the homogeneous stress model predicts that, when E_B is very much larger than E_A, the composite stiffness increases only very gradually with increasing volume fraction until very high volume fractions are reached.

The homogeneous stress model is not only useful for predicting the transverse stiffness of unidirectional layered or fibre composites, but also provides a better predictor (than the homogeneous strain model) of the modulus of particulate-filled composites. This is particularly true where the particles are, on average, equiaxed (i.e. with no preferred direction of alignment) as in concrete, for example. By extension, this also means that a discontinuous fibre-filled composite in which the fibres are randomly oriented is also better described by the homogeneous stress model. The higher the degree of orientation, or alignment of the fibres in such a material, the more its behaviour tends towards that of the homogeneous strain model. Figure 4.9 shows some experimental data obtained on composites of tungsten in copper, together with the bounds of the two models. You can see that, for both continuous and discontinuous aligned wires, the points show excellent agreement with the isostrain solution. The data for dispersed particles of tungsten in copper lie closer to the isostress model solution, although they are not quite coincident with it.

Finally, it is worth pointing out one or two other limitations of these simple models. I have already mentioned that differences in Poisson's ratio can give rise to interface stresses that are not accounted for in our formulations, although these are usually small. One further difficulty is that discontinuous fibres tend to develop tensile stresses across their ends. The stress field around a discontinuous component in a composite can also be modified by stress concentrations due to a component's shape, and due to differences in thermal expansion coefficients. Stress concentrations have two consequences. The first is that the stress can be increased locally to beyond the material yield or fracture stress, leading to premature failure; this effect becomes

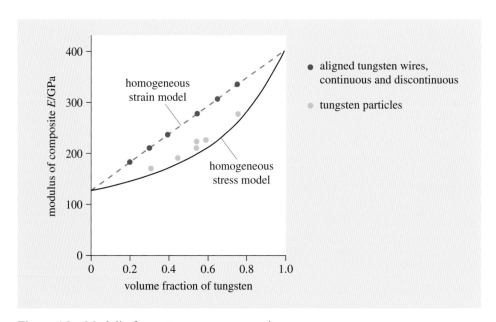

Figure 4.9   Moduli of tungsten–copper composites

more important at higher stresses. The second is that stress concentrations can interact with each other to produce an average stress that is higher than that implied by a simple homogeneous strain model, although this effect becomes significant only between materials with similar moduli. However, the most important effect is probably that of internal (residual) stresses that arise, owing to differences in thermal expansion coefficients of composite materials; this can affect the interlocking mechanical bond between components, particularly polymers.

SAQ 4.3 (Learning outcomes 4.1 and 4.2)

For each of the following materials determine the loading directions, relative to the material's structure, for which the composite modulus might be reasonably predicted using a model based on homogeneous stress and/or homogeneous strain:

(a) plywood

(b) concrete

(c) a glass-fibre composite with continuous fibres aligned in a single direction

(d) a glass-fibre composite with short fibres that are layered in a single plane, but randomly oriented within that plane

(e) a composite of aluminium reinforced with about 20% by volume of approximately spherical silicon carbide particles.

3 EXAMPLE 2: STRESSES AND STRAINS IN THIN-WALLED PRESSURE VESSELS

Next I want to demonstrate how it is possible to construct a simple mathematical model that can be used in the analysis and design of an important type of engineering structure: the pressurized container. Such containers are ubiquitous in the storage and transport of products as diverse as compressed gases and fizzy drinks.

You should already be aware that complex stresses can occur in the walls of pressure vessels, and you have carried out some analysis of a given stress element by assuming that there is a state of plane stress at the surface of the container: see Part 1, Section 5.3 'Transforming plane stress' in this block. However, apart from acknowledging that an internal pressure can give rise to a biaxial stress in the container, we have not explored how the magnitude of these stresses can be predicted, or how they can be used in pressure-vessel design. Now, that might sound like rather a difficult proposition for what appears to be a three-dimensional structure. But, provided that the wall of a pressure vessel is not too thick, it is perfectly reasonable to assume that the two-dimensional plane stress condition applies right the way through the wall, not just at its surface. From there it is possible to build a simple model, widely used by structural engineers, to estimate the stresses and strains in 'thin-walled' pressure vessels. In developing such a model it is necessary to apply the ideas of stress equilibrium and strain compatibility.

Figure 4.10 shows some different sorts of thin-walled container that are commonly used to hold pressurized fluids. Such containers come in two basic shapes. They are either spherical, like the large storage tanks often used for holding liquefied petroleum gas, or more commonly have a cylindrical geometry, as in pressurized air reservoirs, gas canisters, and fire extinguishers. In fact, as you will see in a moment, the sphere is the ideal closure for containing pressurized fluids because the stresses that develop within its walls are lower than for a cylinder of the same thickness; but spheres are often impractical and expensive to form. Cylinders, on the other hand, are easily manufactured from flat plates that are rolled and welded longitudinally. The ends of cylindrical vessels are usually closed off by end-pieces, or 'heads', that must also be welded to the cylindrical body. The cylinder heads may be flat, spherical, ellipsoidal or have more complex curved profiles; the final choice depends on the balance of design considerations with respect to stress distribution and wall thickness, set against the cost of materials and forming.

3.1 Spherical pressure vessels

I have used the subscript 's' for 'sphere' to distinguish some quantities that we will also analyse for a cylinder later.

I will consider the thin-walled, spherical container first, as it is geometrically simpler and will help with analysing the cylindrical container as well. Any internal pressure p acts equally over the entire inner surface of the sphere, thickness t_s (Figure 4.11a), and, because of the symmetry of the vessel, the state of stress in the wall of the sphere must, therefore, be such that there is the same direct stress σ_s in every direction from every point (Figure 4.11b).

Figure 4.10 Various pressure vessels: (a) and (b) spherical and cylindrical storage tanks for liquefied petroleum gas; (c) pressurized CO_2 fire extinguisher; (d) air receiver for compressed-air storage; (e) telescopic gas holder for maintaining constant mains gas pressure for domestic use; (f) aerosol cans

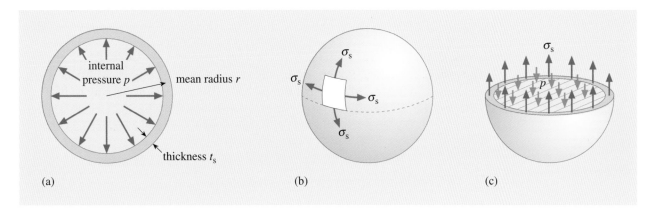

Figure 4.11 (a) Spherical container under uniform internal pressure; (b) and (c) stresses in the wall of the pressurized container

Note that Figure 4.11 indicates that I have made the two-dimensional assumption of plane stress in the thin wall of the vessel. In reality, there is a compressive stress equal to the internal pressure acting on the inner surface and pointing towards the centre of the sphere. However, as you will see in a moment, I can always make sure that I use this type of analysis only under conditions for which I know that p is very much smaller than σ_s, and so can be ignored. In other words, my plane stress assumption, although not absolutely correct, is nevertheless valid for modelling purposes.

So, assuming that I have a spherical pressure vessel of known radius r and wall thickness t_s, filled with a gas to a uniform pressure p, how do I go about determining the magnitude of the stress σ_s in its walls? Well, I can do this by making an imaginary cut through a diameter of the sphere and then considering how the forces must balance across one of the hemispheres – in other words, by applying the principle of force equilibrium.

Picture a cut along the dashed line of Figure 4.11(b) so that one half of the sphere, together with the pressurized gas inside it, is isolated from the other half as shown in Figure 4.11(c). Now, think about the stresses that would need to be applied to keep the hemisphere and its contents in equilibrium. Clearly, a downward pressure p is necessary to keep the gas confined in the lower half, and this pressure acts on a circular area πr^2. But this pressure can't act alone if equilibrium conditions are to be met; it must be opposed by an upward stress. This can come only from the wall of the vessel itself: the stress σ_s acting in the ring of radius r and thickness t_s through which I have made the cut, that has an area of $2\pi r t_s$.

So, if I assume that the pressure vessel isn't moving, then in order to maintain vertical equilibrium the downward force due to the pressure in Figure 4.11(c) must be equal to the upward force due to the stress:

$$\text{downward pressure} \times \text{internal area} = \text{upward stress} \times \text{wall area}$$
$$p \times \pi r^2 = \sigma_s \times 2\pi r t_s$$

giving

$$\sigma_s = \frac{pr}{2t_s} \tag{4.6}$$

The interesting thing about Equation (4.6) is that it shows that the stress in the walls of the pressure vessel has no dependence on the properties of the material from which it is made; for instance, there is no elastic modulus term. Only the pressure and the geometry influence the stress.

I can now try and justify my earlier plane stress assumption, which depended on p being small compared with σ. Suppose I stipulate that p should amount to no more than, say, 10%, or 1/10th, of σ. Rearranging Equation (4.6) gives:

$$\frac{p}{\sigma_s} = 2\frac{t_s}{r}$$

and so the condition becomes:

$$\frac{2t_s}{r} \leq \frac{1}{10} \quad \text{or} \quad \frac{t_s}{r} \leq \frac{1}{20}$$

In other words, the wall thickness must be at least 20 times smaller than the radius of the vessel. Hence, I've also defined what I mean by 'thin-walled' in this case. In fact, to minimize the amount of material used, many spherical gas containers quite ordinarily have a radius-to-thickness ratio that is 150 or more.

EXERCISE 4.3

Figure 4.12 shows the construction of one of the worlds largest spherical gas storage tanks, 34 m in diameter and made from a total of 126 high-tensile steel plates, each measuring 12 m by 3 m by 35 mm thick. In order to construct the sphere, each of the plates is trapezoidal in shape, and slightly curved.

If the tensile stress in the walls of such a vessel is not to exceed 400 MPa, estimate the maximum allowable internal pressure that it could sustain.

Figure 4.12   Construction of a 34 m diameter, spherical gas tank

SAQ 4.4 (Learning outcomes 4.1 and 4.3)

Liquefied petroleum gas (LPG) fuels, usually mixtures of primarily butane and propane, are commonly stored in large, pressurized, spherical containers (e.g. Figure 4.10a) while they await distribution. The pressure ensures that the fuel remains in liquefied form.

One such container, 10 m in diameter, was designed to withstand internal pressures of up to 2.0 MPa, typical for this type of application.

(a) Calculate the wall thickness of the vessel, assuming the design was based on a plane stress assumption with a uniform internal pressure amounting to no more than 1% of the shell stress.

(b) Why might the assumption of a uniform internal pressure be incorrect for large, liquid-containing vessels?

(c) The pressure at the bottom of a column of fluid of height h is given by $\rho g h$, where ρ is the density of the liquid and g is the acceleration due to gravity, 9.8 m s^{-2}. Calculate the pressure at the bottom of a 10 m column of liquid petroleum with a density of 550 kg m^{-3}, and compare it with the internal pressure in the container.

3.2 Cylindrical pressure vessels

Now let's turn our attention to a pressure vessel consisting of a circular cylinder with spherical end caps, as shown in Figure 4.13(a). First of all, note that Equation (4.6) still holds for the hemispherical end caps. The cylinder could be lifted out and the two hemispheres brought together to form an entire sphere such as we have just analysed. This would in no way disturb the conditions in the end caps, so the spherical pressure vessel analysis must apply to them.

However, in the body of the cylinder the stresses and strains are not the same in all directions as they were for the sphere. To characterize the stress state we need to determine the stress on a small element on the wall of the cylinder with its sides parallel and perpendicular to the cylinder axis. In Figure 4.13(a) the stress on this element parallel to the cylinder axis is called the *axial stress* σ_a and that perpendicular to the axis is called the *circumferential* or *hoop stress* σ_h (because it is the stress component found in hoops used to bind the slats in old wooden barrels). It is necessary to determine components in the circumferential and axial directions relative to the cylindrical geometry. Because of the symmetry of the cylindrical container there is no shear stress exerted on this particular element; hence, the axial and hoop stresses are *principal stresses*.

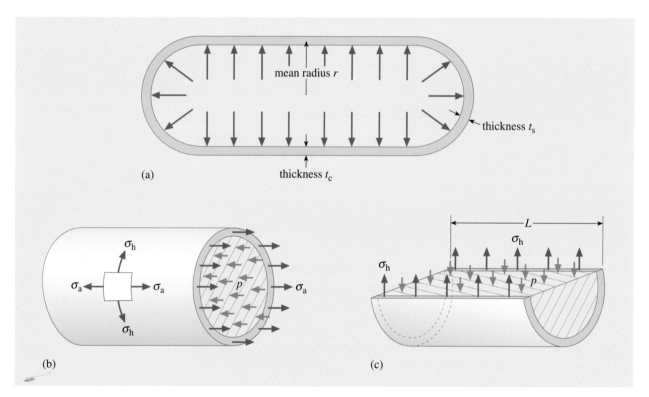

Figure 4.13 Thin-walled pressurized cylindrical container: (a) vessel consisting of a circular cylinder with cylindrical end caps; (b) transverse section through the cylinder, giving the axial stress; (c) isolation of a part of the shell, giving the hoop stress

Dealing first with the stress in the axial direction, I will make an imaginary cut, just as I did for the sphere, so that I end up with a body as shown in Figure 4.13(b). Notice that the forces that must be balanced to give horizontal equilibrium in this free body resemble those that we deduced must apply to the hemisphere in Figure 4.11(c). Hence, simply by putting t_c, the thickness of the cylinder, in place of t_s, and σ_a in place of σ_s in Equation (4.6), we get:

$$\sigma_a = \frac{pr}{2t_c} \tag{4.7}$$

To determine the circumferential or hoop stress σ_h I can cut out the body shown in Figure 4.13(c). Compressed gas is contained within this portion of the cylinder by two transverse planes separated by a distance L, and by a horizontal plane through the axis of the cylinder. The horizontal stresses acting on the cross-sectional planes are not shown in this diagram because, to get the result I need, it is only necessary to consider the vertical equilibrium of the body.

For vertical equilibrium, then, the downward pressure p acting over an area $2rL$ must be reacted by an upward force given by the hoop stress σ_h acting on an area $2Lt_c$. Hence:

$$p2rL = \sigma_h 2Lt_c$$

so

$$\sigma_h = \frac{pr}{t_c} \tag{4.8}$$

which, by comparison with Equation (4.7), is exactly twice the axial stress.

SAQ 4.5 (Learning outcome 4.3)

A cylindrical steel boiler, of wall thickness 1 cm and diameter 1 m, is subjected to an internal pressure of 1 MPa.

(a) Determine the axial and hoop stresses in the walls of the cylinder.

(b) Recall that the axial and hoop stresses in a cylindrical vessel are principal stresses. Sketch Mohr's circle for the stresses you calculated in part (a) and determine the maximum shear stress in the surface of the cylinder.

Now let's turn to strain. In order to estimate the axial strain at a point on the circumference of our cylindrical container it is necessary to realize that this will have two contributions. The first of these is due to the direct tensile stress σ_a applied in the axial direction and, assuming the cylinder is made from a linear-elastic material, this first contribution is an extension equal to σ_a/E.

The second contribution is due to the effect of Poisson's ratio v for the material of the cylinder. The hoop stress σ_h in the direction at right angles to the one we are considering will produce a tensile strain of σ_h/E in the hoop direction of action. But the Poisson effect dictates that this will also produce a strain of $-\nu\sigma_h/E$ (a contraction) transverse to this, i.e. in the axial direction. Therefore, the total strain in the axial direction is:

$$\varepsilon_a = \frac{\sigma_a}{E} - \nu\frac{\sigma_h}{E}$$

and substituting for σ_a and σ_h from Equations (4.7) and (4.8) respectively gives:

$$\varepsilon_a = \frac{pr}{2t_cE} - \frac{\nu pr}{t_cE}$$

which can be written more concisely as:

$$\varepsilon_a = \frac{pr}{2t_cE}(1-2\nu) \qquad (4.9)$$

Similarly, the hoop strain ε_h is given by:

$$\varepsilon_h = \frac{\sigma_h}{E} - \nu\frac{\sigma_a}{E} = \frac{pr}{t_cE} - \frac{\nu pr}{2t_cE}$$

that is,

$$\varepsilon_h = \frac{pr}{2t_cE}(2-\nu) \qquad (4.10)$$

In the case of the *sphere*, the surface strain is the same in all directions and both contributions come from the stress σ_s:

$$\varepsilon_s = \frac{\sigma_s}{E} - \nu\frac{\sigma_s}{E} = \frac{\sigma_s}{E}(1-\nu)$$

and substituting for σ_s using Equation (4.6) produces:

$$\varepsilon_s = \frac{pr}{2t_sE}(1-\nu) \qquad (4.11)$$

EXERCISE 4.4

Consider again the 1 m diameter, 1 cm thick, cylindrical steel boiler of SAQ 4.5.

(a) Assuming the same 1 MPa internal pressure as before, determine the axial and hoop strains in the walls of the cylinder (take $E = 200$ GPa, $\nu = 0.3$).

(b) Calculate the axial and hoop strains in a spherical vessel of the same diameter and thickness, made of the same material and subject to the same internal pressure.

Exercise 4.4 illustrates that the strains within a spherical pressure vessel are not the same as those in the cylindrical walls of a vessel of the same radius, wall thickness and internal pressure. Hence, if we were to try and construct a steel vessel like that in Figure 4.13, with a cylindrical mid-section capped by two hemispheres, using the same thickness of material throughout, we would encounter the problem of *compatibility of strains*. The largest difference occurs in the circumferential, or hoop, direction. Unless the hoop strain in the hemispherical ends, given by Equation (4.11), is equal to that in the cylindrical mid-section (given by Equation 4.10), then, as the pressure is built up in the vessel, forces and stress will arise that have not been allowed for in the above analysis.

The difficulty can be eliminated at the design stage by an appropriate choice of thicknesses. Setting $\varepsilon_s = \varepsilon_h$, so that the strains in the hoop direction are compatible, we have from Equations (4.10) and (4.11):

$$\frac{pr}{2t_sE}(1-v) = \frac{pr}{2t_cE}(2-v)$$

from which the ratio of thicknesses is given by:

$$\frac{t_c}{t_s} = \frac{2-v}{1-v}$$

SAQ 4.6 (Learning outcomes 4.1 and 4.3)

Once again refer to the cylindrical pressure vessel you analysed in SAQ 4.5 and Exercise 4.4.

In order to maintain strain compatibility between the cylindrical and spherical parts of the vessel, what must be the thickness of the end caps if the cylinder walls are 1 cm thick?

SAQ 4.7 (Learning outcome 4.3)

A standard fizzy-drinks can (Figure 4.14), 6.6 cm in diameter, contains liquid at an internal pressure of around 300 kPa. Imagine that you are part of a team responsible for designing a cylindrical container using an aluminium alloy that has a uniaxial yield stress of 250 MPa and a tensile fracture strength of 320 MPa.

Your job is to estimate the minimum thickness of sheet that should be used for the uniform cylindrical walls of the container if you are concerned about failure by:

(a) tensile fracture

(b) yield (use the Tresca criterion).

Apply a safety factor of 2 in both cases.

Hint: You can ignore the flat end closures of the can in your analysis; these are to be designed and manufactured separately before being joined to the cylindrical body. Such flat plates resist the internal pressure by bending.

Figure 4.14 Pressurized drinks can

The Tresca criterion was introduced in Part 3, Section 6.1 of this block.

4 EXAMPLE 3: HOW THE FINITE ELEMENT METHOD WORKS

In this final example I will look at a broad modelling technique rather than a specific structural application.

The finite element method is a powerful numerical tool for determining stresses and strains in structures that are too complex to model by so-called 'analytical' methods alone, for instance in cases where it is not easy to write down an equation, or a set of equations, to describe the structural behaviour. It is increasingly expected of engineers that they should be at least comfortable with interpreting and using the results from finite element analyses. To this end, we have already examined several examples so far in this course. But you may feel that modelling of this type, which involves the application of complicated computer software that the user need never understand, is like using a 'black box'. Something goes in one end and an answer comes out the other, but who knows what goes on in between? Well, in this section I want to give you the opportunity to look inside that box.

Although I've just said that the finite element method is used when equations can't be written down, that's not to say that the method doesn't use equations itself. In fact it does: it can use thousands of them, all of which have to be solved simultaneously to arrive at a solution for the structure as a whole. The key mathematical concept underlying finite element analysis concerns the way data in these equations are stored and manipulated – using *matrices*. In the following sections I want to take you through some very simple finite element analysis using a technique called the *matrix stiffness method*. To follow this you will need to know a little about how numbers can be stored and manipulated using matrices. If you are unfamiliar with matrices, or just want to refresh your memory, I've provide a summary of everything you need to know in ☑ **Matrix methods for finite element analysis** ☑. You can either read that section now, or refer back to it as necessary.

☑ Matrix methods for finite element analysis

A matrix is simply a rectangular array of numbers arranged in rows and columns, such as:

$$[C] = \begin{bmatrix} 2 & 1 & -3 \\ 4 & 7 & 5 \end{bmatrix} \text{ or } [\sigma] = \begin{bmatrix} 10 & 2 & 1 \\ 2 & 5 & 3 \\ 1 & 3 & 5 \end{bmatrix} \text{MPa}$$

where $[C]$ is a matrix of two rows and three columns and $[\sigma]$ is a 'square' matrix with equal numbers of rows and columns, three in this case. Matrices can also have a single row or column, in which case they are also called vectors. For example:

$$\{D\} = \{10 \quad 24 \quad -9\} \text{ or } \{F\} = \begin{Bmatrix} 100 \\ 0 \\ 0 \end{Bmatrix}$$

☑

where $\{D\}$ is a row vector and $\{F\}$ is a column vector. Note that I have chosen to use curly brackets to distinguish vectors from other matrices; the distinction is sometimes useful, as you will see later.

Matrices, vectors and scalars (single numbers) are all different types of tensor, following certain rules of manipulation (tensor is the mathematical term for a grouping of numbers that helps to formulate and solve problems). In this course you have already met the stress tensor, a square matrix for storing the nine stress components necessary for three-dimensional stress analysis, and you may also have had to deal with matrices or arrays of numbers elsewhere. Rather than provide a complete summary of matrix algebra, I just want to review a couple of simple manipulations. To help understand the basics of finite element analysis we will just need to use information stored either in square matrices, like $[\sigma]$, or in column vectors, like $\{F\}$. Hence, I just want to review how to carry out multiplication using arrays of this type.

Multiplication of a square matrix or column vector by a number is simple; just multiply each component of the array by the number. For example:

$$5[C] = 5\begin{bmatrix} 2 & 1 & -3 \\ 4 & 7 & 5 \end{bmatrix} = \begin{bmatrix} 10 & 5 & -15 \\ 20 & 35 & 25 \end{bmatrix}$$

$$12\,000\{F\} = 12\,000 \begin{Bmatrix} 100 \\ 0 \\ 0 \end{Bmatrix} = \begin{Bmatrix} 1\,200\,000 \\ 0 \\ 0 \end{Bmatrix} = \begin{Bmatrix} 1.2 \\ 0 \\ 0 \end{Bmatrix} \times 10^6$$

Multiplication of a square matrix by a column vector is only slightly trickier. For this to work, the column vector must be the same height as the square matrix. The procedure involves multiplying the components in each row of the matrix by the corresponding components in the column vector, and then summing them. The answers, one for each row, form a new column matrix the same size as the old one. Note that the order of multiplication is important here: this procedure will work only if the square matrix is multiplied by the column vector and *not* the other way round. Here's an example where a square matrix of two rows and columns is multiplied by a column vector of two rows (I've used letters and subscripts, and highlighted the computation for the first row, to help you see how the multiplication works):

$$\begin{bmatrix} a_1 & a_2 \\ b_1 & b_2 \end{bmatrix} \begin{Bmatrix} x_1 \\ x_2 \end{Bmatrix} = \begin{Bmatrix} a_1x_1 + a_2x_2 \\ b_1x_1 + b_2x_2 \end{Bmatrix}$$

or, using numbers:

$$\begin{bmatrix} 1 & 2 \\ 3 & 4 \end{bmatrix} \begin{Bmatrix} 5 \\ 6 \end{Bmatrix} = \begin{Bmatrix} (1\times5) + (2\times6) \\ (3\times5) + (4\times6) \end{Bmatrix} = \begin{Bmatrix} 5+12 \\ 15+24 \end{Bmatrix} = \begin{Bmatrix} 17 \\ 39 \end{Bmatrix}$$

Similarly, for a three-row square matrix:

$$\begin{bmatrix} a_1 & a_2 & a_3 \\ b_1 & b_2 & b_3 \\ c_1 & c_2 & c_3 \end{bmatrix} \begin{Bmatrix} x_1 \\ x_2 \\ x_3 \end{Bmatrix} = \begin{Bmatrix} a_1x_1 + a_2x_2 + a_3x_3 \\ b_1x_1 + b_2x_2 + b_3x_3 \\ c_1x_1 + c_2x_2 + c_3x_3 \end{Bmatrix}$$

and again with numbers:

$$\begin{bmatrix} 1 & 2 & 3 \\ 4 & 5 & 6 \\ 7 & 8 & 9 \end{bmatrix} \begin{bmatrix} 10 \\ 20 \\ 30 \end{bmatrix} = \begin{Bmatrix} (1 \times 10) + (2 \times 20) + (3 \times 30) \\ (4 \times 10) + (5 \times 20) + (6 \times 30) \\ (7 \times 10) + (8 \times 20) + (9 \times 30) \end{Bmatrix} = \begin{bmatrix} 10 + 40 + 90 \\ 40 + 100 + 180 \\ 70 + 160 + 270 \end{bmatrix} = \begin{Bmatrix} 140 \\ 320 \\ 500 \end{Bmatrix}$$

If you've never used matrices before then you might find these procedures rather odd. However, it turns out these matrix manipulations provide a very compact means of handling large datasets. If you need practice, have a go at the following exercises; if you can do these then you will be able to follow the rest of this section.

EXERCISE 4.5

Perform the following matrix calculations:

(a) $\quad 3 \begin{Bmatrix} 9 \\ 12 \\ 6 \end{Bmatrix}$

(b) $\quad \dfrac{1}{3} \begin{bmatrix} 9 & 3 & 0 \\ 3 & 12 & 3 \\ 0 & 3 & 6 \end{bmatrix}$

(c) $\quad \dfrac{1}{3} \begin{Bmatrix} 0.009 \\ 0.012 \\ 0.006 \end{Bmatrix} \times 10^3$

Multiply out the following to form a single column vector:

(d) $\quad \begin{bmatrix} 2 & 1 \\ 3 & 10 \end{bmatrix} \begin{Bmatrix} 5 \\ 4 \end{Bmatrix}$

(e) $\quad \begin{bmatrix} 1 & -1 \\ -1 & 1 \end{bmatrix} \begin{Bmatrix} 5 \\ 4 \end{Bmatrix}$

(f) $\quad \begin{bmatrix} 6 & -6 & 0 \\ -6 & 9 & -3 \\ 0 & -3 & 3 \end{bmatrix} \begin{Bmatrix} 1 \\ 0 \\ 1 \end{Bmatrix}$

4.1 Simple bar under uniaxial tension

I will start by considering a simple bar of uniform geometry and composition, as shown in Figure 4.15(a). Assuming that the bar is free to move and transmit forces in one direction only, along its axis, then I have set out the basis for a *one-dimensional* model of reality. This model can be represented using a single finite element, as presented in Figure 4.15(b), with the end points of the bar element marked by two *nodes*. These nodes act as connectors, ensuring *compatibility* between elements, and can also supply an interface to the outside world, allowing external loads to be applied, for example. In Figure 4.15(b) I have labelled the nodes numerically (that is the usual convention) and chosen them to lie in the direction of a horizontal x-axis.

Although this is a one-dimensional model that only allows axial forces and displacements, note that the real rod is still a three-dimensional entity: it has a cross-sectional area extending into the y- and z-directions, for example.

In the case of the bar model in Figure 4.15(a), assuming elastic deformation, it is a simple matter to write down an expression linking force F and total displacement ΔL across the whole of the bar, provided that the initial geometry (length L, cross-sectional area A) and material properties (elastic modulus E) are known. From the definition of elastic modulus:

Only the elastic modulus is needed here, since Poisson's ratio tells us about deformation in the transverse directions, with which our model is not concerned.

$$E = \frac{\sigma}{\varepsilon} = \frac{F/A}{\Delta L/L} = \frac{FL}{A\Delta L}$$

and rearranging gives:

$$F = \frac{AE}{L}\Delta L \tag{4.12}$$

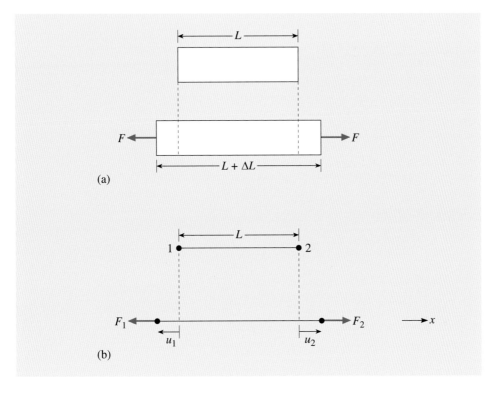

Figure 4.15 One-dimensional model for (a) an axially loaded uniform bar and (b) the equivalent finite element

Now, for the finite element model of Figure 4.15(b) it is necessary to approach things a little differently. I can't start by considering the model as a whole: I need first to quantify the forces and displacements at every node. That's because this single element would normally be part of a much larger 'mesh' of elements, connected by many nodes. Finite element analysis works by putting together all the equations that apply to every individual node in order to come to a solution that also works for the entire mesh. Hence, in Figure 4.15(b), it is important to distinguish between the net forces F_1 and F_2, which apply at nodes 1 and 2 respectively, and between the corresponding nodal displacements u_1 and u_2.

So let's look at things from the point of view of node 1 first. I need to come up with an expression like Equation (4.12), but using nodal displacements to describe the change in length of the element. Displacements, like forces, are vector quantities, so it's necessary to consider their direction and their magnitude. Looking again at Figure 4.15, the total change in length of the element *measured in the direction of* F_1 is the sum of the individual vector displacements:

$$\Delta L = u_1 + \left(-u_2\right) = u_1 - u_2$$

and so Equation (4.12) can be rewritten to describe the deformation caused by the force at node 1:

$$F_1 = \frac{AE}{L}\left(u_1 - u_2\right) \tag{4.13}$$

Similarly, the total change in length of the element measured in the direction of F_2 is $\left(-u_1 + u_2\right)$; hence, from the point of view of node 2:

$$F_2 = \frac{AE}{L}\left(-u_1 + u_2\right) \tag{4.14}$$

And that's it! Equations (4.13) and (4.14) provide a complete description of the nodal forces and displacements in the single-element model we have been considering. Because this is a simple example, you can see clearly the similarity between these results and the result from the entire bar in Equation (4.12).

EXERCISE 4.6

Consider a one-dimensional, single finite element model of a steel bar ($L = 300$ mm, $A = 10$ mm^2, $E = 300$ GPa) of the type shown in Figure 4.15. Calculate the nodal forces *measured with respect to the x-coordinate system* when the nodal displacements are:

(a) $u_1 = -0.1$ mm and $u_2 = 0.1$ mm

(b) $u_1 = 0.1$ mm and $u_2 = -0.1$ mm

(c) $u_1 = 0.1$ mm and $u_2 = 0.1$ mm.

Comment on the loading in each case, given that a positive force acts in the positive x-direction and a negative force acts in the negative x-direction.

Writing out a set of simultaneous equations, one for each node, is fine for a single element. When there are hundreds or thousands of nodes it makes sense to devise a more compact way of organizing and storing the model data. In fact, for finite element analysis, the two nodal equations can be combined into a single expression using matrices:

$$\begin{Bmatrix} F_1 \\ F_2 \end{Bmatrix} = \frac{AE}{L} \begin{bmatrix} 1 & -1 \\ -1 & 1 \end{bmatrix} \begin{Bmatrix} u_1 \\ u_2 \end{Bmatrix} \qquad (4.15)$$

which is identical to Equations (4.13) and (4.14). If you're unfamiliar with matrix operations take a look at the short summary 'Matrix methods for finite element analysis', if you haven't done so already, and try Exercise 4.7.

EXERCISE 4.7

Demonstrate to yourself that Equation (4.15) is equivalent to Equations (4.13) and (4.14) in the following way:

(a) First, multiply out the square matrix and the column vector on the right-hand side of Equation (4.15) to get a new column vector.

(b) Next, rewrite Equation (4.15) using this new vector.

(c) Finally, compare the first and second rows of your new vector equation with Equation (4.13) and Equation (4.14).

So, matrices and vectors provide a neat way of reformulating sets of equations. In fact, Equation (4.15) can be written even more compactly as:

$$\{F\} = [k]\{u\} \qquad (4.16)$$

where $\{F\}$ is a column vector of nodal forces, $\{u\}$ is a column vector of nodal displacements and $[k]$ is the *stiffness matrix*:

$$[k] = \frac{AE}{L} \begin{bmatrix} 1 & -1 \\ -1 & 1 \end{bmatrix} = \begin{bmatrix} AE/L & -AE/L \\ -AE/L & AE/L \end{bmatrix} \qquad (4.17)$$

which is the key to efficient storage of finite element data on a computer. The terms along the 'leading diagonal' of the stiffness matrix contain information about the force per unit displacement at every node in the finite element mesh. All the other 'off-diagonal' terms represent the force at one node due to unit deflection at another node. Stiffness matrices are always symmetric; that is, the terms are mirrored across the leading diagonal. Because of this, it is necessary to store only one half of the matrix during computer analysis, thus saving computer storage space and time in accessing and retrieving data.

The 'leading diagonal' is the diagonal that runs from the top left corner to the bottom right corner of the matrix.

4.2 Stepped bar under uniaxial tension

Of course, there's not really much point in using the matrix stiffness approach for analysing the deformation of a single finite element in the way I've just shown you.

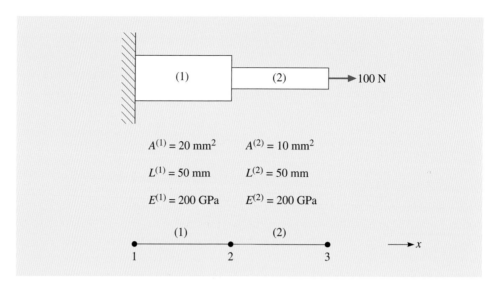

Figure 4.16   One-dimensional model for (a) an axially loaded stepped bar and (b) the equivalent finite element model

The real beauty of the technique starts to become apparent if we try something a little more complicated. As an illustration, I'll analyse the stepped bar structure sketched in Figure 4.16. The bar, fixed at one end and with a tensile load at its other free end, is made from a single piece of steel with a change in cross-sectional area halfway along its length. I will model this using two finite elements, labelled (1) and (2), as shown in the figure.

The idea is that, given the information in Figure 4.16, I will determine the unknown forces and displacements at all points in the finite element mesh, i.e. at nodes 1, 2 and 3. To do this, I will follow the approach used generally in finite element analysis. In particular, I will determine stiffness matrices for each of the elements and then assemble them into a *global* stiffness matrix that simulates the deformation of the entire structure. I will also need to take into account the *boundary conditions* applied to my model; these include any external applied forces and any constraints imposed on the movement of certain nodes.

For element (1), Equation (4.17) gives the stiffness matrix as:

$$
\begin{aligned}
\left[k^{(1)}\right] &= \frac{A^{(1)}E^{(1)}}{L^{(1)}}\begin{bmatrix} 1 & -1 \\ -1 & 1 \end{bmatrix} \\
&= \frac{20\times10^{-6}\ \mathrm{m}^2\times200\times10^{9}\ \mathrm{N\ m}^{-2}}{0.05\ \mathrm{m}}\begin{bmatrix} 1 & -1 \\ -1 & 1 \end{bmatrix} \\
&= 8\times10^{7}\begin{bmatrix} 1 & -1 \\ -1 & 1 \end{bmatrix}\mathrm{N\ m}^{-1} \\
&= \begin{bmatrix} 8 & -8 \\ -8 & 8 \end{bmatrix}\times10^{7}\ \mathrm{N\ m}^{-1}
\end{aligned}
$$

and for element (2):

$$\left[k^{(2)}\right] = \frac{A^{(2)}E^{(2)}}{L^{(2)}}\begin{bmatrix} 1 & -1 \\ -1 & 1 \end{bmatrix}$$

$$= \frac{10 \times 10^{-6} \text{ m}^2 \times 200 \times 10^9 \text{ N m}^{-2}}{0.05 \text{ m}}\begin{bmatrix} 1 & -1 \\ -1 & 1 \end{bmatrix}$$

$$= \begin{bmatrix} 4 & -4 \\ -4 & 4 \end{bmatrix} \times 10^7 \text{ N m}^{-1}$$

Now, the stiffness matrix $[k^{(1)}]$ for element (1) contains information about nodes 1 and 2, and the stiffness matrix $[k^{(2)}]$ for element (2) contains information about nodes 2 and 3. The next step is to put these two together to make a stiffness matrix for the whole structure. You've seen that the matrices for elements with two nodes have two rows and two columns, hence the matrix for a structure with three nodes ought to have three rows and three columns. In fact, it is possible to store all the information about element stiffness in a single matrix in the following way:

$$\left[k^{(1)}\right] = \begin{matrix} & u_1 & u_2 \\ & \begin{bmatrix} 8 & -8 \\ -8 & 8 \end{bmatrix} & \begin{matrix} u_1 \\ u_2 \end{matrix} \end{matrix} \times 10^7 \text{ N m}^{-1} \qquad \left[k^{(2)}\right] = \begin{matrix} & u_2 & u_3 \\ & \begin{bmatrix} 4 & -4 \\ -4 & 4 \end{bmatrix} & \begin{matrix} u_2 \\ u_3 \end{matrix} \end{matrix} \times 10^7 \text{ N m}^{-1}$$

$$\left[k\right] = \begin{matrix} & u_1 & u_2 & u_3 \\ & \begin{bmatrix} 8 & -8 & 0 \\ -8 & 8+4 & -4 \\ 0 & -4 & 4 \end{bmatrix} & \begin{matrix} u_1 \\ u_2 \\ u_3 \end{matrix} \end{matrix} \times 10^7 \text{ N m}^{-1}$$

where $[k]$ is the global stiffness matrix for both elements combined. Note that, because node 2 is common to both elements, the (u_2, u_2) position in the global stiffness matrix contains a contribution from both element stiffness matrices. Also notice that no terms appear at the positions in $[k]$ that link nodes 1 and 3; these nodes are not connected in the finite element model, and so their stiffnesses have been set to zero.

Next, I can insert the global stiffness matrix into the force–displacement Equation (4.16):

$$\{F\} = [k]\{u\}$$

i.e.

$$\begin{Bmatrix} F_1 \\ F_2 \\ F_3 \end{Bmatrix} = \begin{bmatrix} 8 & -8 & 0 \\ -8 & 12 & -4 \\ 0 & -4 & 4 \end{bmatrix} \begin{Bmatrix} u_1 \\ u_2 \\ u_3 \end{Bmatrix} \times 10^7 \qquad (4.18)$$

and I appear to be left with six 'unknowns' to find: three forces and three displacements. But I already have information about some of these unknowns; such prior knowledge provides the boundary conditions of the finite element model. In Figure 4.16 there is an applied force at node 3, $F_3 = 100$ N and, because the bar is fixed at its left-hand end, it is also evident that there must be a reaction force at node 1. Assuming equilibrium, it is obvious in this instance what that reaction force should be, but I'm going to calculate it in any case to demonstrate the general finite element method for determining unknown forces. There is no applied force at node 2, so $F_2 = 0$. Furthermore, because node 1 is fixed, there is no displacement there and $u_1 = 0$.

Inserting all these boundary conditions into Equation (4.18) gives:

$$\begin{Bmatrix} F_1 \\ 0 \\ 100 \end{Bmatrix} = \begin{bmatrix} 8 & -8 & 0 \\ -8 & 12 & -4 \\ 0 & -4 & 4 \end{bmatrix} \begin{Bmatrix} 0 \\ u_2 \\ u_3 \end{Bmatrix} \times 10^7 \text{ N} \tag{4.19}$$

which can be multiplied out to give three simultaneous equations that can then be solved for the three unknowns F_1, u_2 and u_3.

EXERCISE 4.8

Use the following procedure to determine the unknown nodal forces and displacements in the finite element model of Figure 4.16.

(a) Multiply out the matrix Equation (4.19) to obtain a set of three simultaneous equations. The numbers are easier to handle if you start with the equation in the following form:

$$\begin{Bmatrix} F_1 \\ 0 \\ 100 \end{Bmatrix} \times 10^{-7} = \begin{bmatrix} 8 & -8 & 0 \\ -8 & 12 & -4 \\ 0 & -4 & 4 \end{bmatrix} \begin{Bmatrix} 0 \\ u_2 \\ u_3 \end{Bmatrix}$$

and ignore units while you're writing out the terms.

(b) Solve for the displacements u_2 and u_3 using the second and third equations you obtained from part (a).

(c) Substitute for displacement in the first equation to determine the reaction force F_1.

Although finite element computations are carried out using forces and displacements, results for engineering analysis are usually presented as stresses and strains, computed on an element-by-element basis. The following question leads you through this and also asks you to check the finite element solution using a more conventional calculation.

SAQ 4.8 (Learning outcome 4.4)

Calculate the stresses and strains in the two finite elements of the one-dimensional stepped-bar model presented in Figure 4.16, using the forces and displacements you computed in your answer to Exercise 4.8. Proceed in the following way:

(a) Given that the change in length of element (1) in the positive x-direction is $(-u_1 + u_2)$, and that of element (2) in the same direction is $(-u_2 + u_3)$, calculate the elemental strains $\varepsilon^{(1)}$ and $\varepsilon^{(2)}$ in these directions.

Recall the discussion surrounding Equations (4.13) and (4.14) if you want to convince yourself that these expressions are correct.

(b) Calculate the associated elemental stresses, $\sigma^{(1)}$ and $\sigma^{(2)}$, using Hooke's law.

(c) Check your answers to part (b) by calculating the theoretical stress in each part of the bar from the applied force and cross-sectional area.

If I really wanted to analyse the stresses and strains in a stepped bar I would probably need to pay a bit more attention to its exact geometry. It is unlikely that the component, if it were intended to bear any significant load, would have a sharp change of section as this would lead to a severe stress concentration at the step. It is more likely to have a fillet radius, as shown in the two-dimensional finite element model of Figure 4.17. Here, the stress is highly variable in the vicinity of the fillet but fairly uniform elsewhere, tending towards the stresses we have calculated using our one-dimensional simplification. For comparison, the stresses predicted by the one-dimensional and two-dimensional models along a line down the central axis of the bar are shown in Figure 4.18.

The step-by-step analysis I have taken you through in this section, although a very simple application of the finite element technique, nevertheless demonstrates the procedures used in more complex equilibrium analyses: the discretization of the problem into a mesh of elements, the formation of element matrices and vectors, the combination of this elemental information to form global equations, the application of boundary conditions and finally the solution of the equations to determine unknown forces and displacements. However, it is worth pointing out that we were able to carry out an *exact* finite element analysis of the one-dimensional model we constructed (see your solutions to SAQ 4.8); in practice, this isn't usually the case. For intricate two- and three-dimensional models, subjected to more complicated loading, it is practically impossible to determine the nodal displacements exactly. This is because solving a large set of equations for many variables requires special iterative solution techniques that rely on incremental convergence towards a 'correct' solution. For this reason, practical finite element models for engineering applications

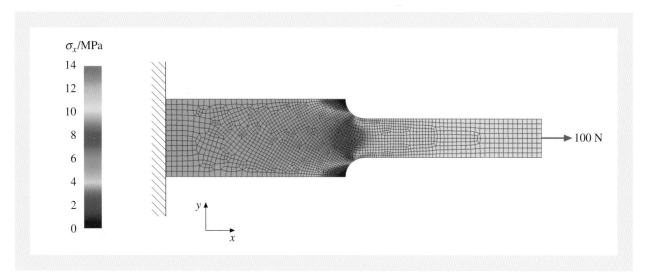

Figure 4.17   Two-dimensional finite element model of an axially loaded stepped bar, analogous to the one-dimensional model presented in Figure 4.16

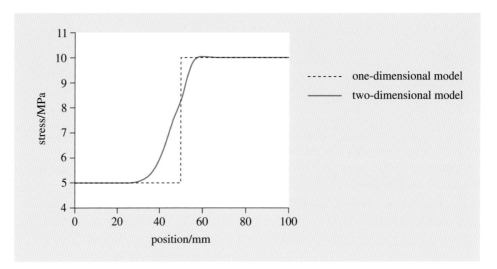

Figure 4.18   Predicted stresses along midline of the stepped bar using one-dimensional and two-dimensional finite element analysis

really provide only approximate solutions to any given problem. In reality, a balance must be struck between accuracy, which can be improved by using large numbers of elements, and cost, as determined by the amount of computing power and time that can be spared in deriving a solution.

5 SUMMARY – AND A USEFUL TIP

My aim in this part of the course has been to show how the basic concepts of stress and strain that we have been working with can be applied to a wide range of components, materials and problems. They can be used to describe the behaviour of reinforced concrete, calculate the stress in the wall of a pressure vessel, and provide the basis for one of the most powerful tools in modern structural analysis.

Engineers have been studying stresses in components and structures of all shapes and sizes for a very long time indeed, and much of the knowledge and wisdom that has been accumulated has been compiled and tabulated in books full of standard solutions. So, for example, it is not really necessary to carry out finite element analysis of a simple stepped bar, regardless of how it is loaded, because the nominal stress can be easily calculated and, more importantly, the stress concentration can be derived from widely available handbooks.

SAQ 4.9 (Learning outcome 4.5)

A stepped flat tension bar, similar to that which we considered in SAQ 4.8, has cross-sectional areas of 10 mm² and 20 mm² and an applied tensile load of 100 N.

Using Figure 4.19, reproduced from Block 1 Part 3, estimate the maximum stress in the component if it is 1 mm thick and has a fillet radius of 1 mm at each shoulder.

Figure 4.19 Stress concentration factors for a uniaxially loaded flat bar with shoulder fillets

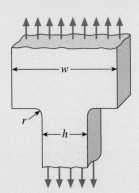

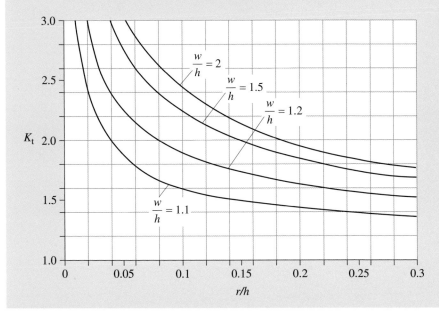

So do not underestimate the power of mathematical analysis to give insight into the behaviour of structures, and to provide back-of-the-envelope checks to the outputs from complex computer-based modelling. In situations where an estimate of the stress in a component is needed, it may be a lot faster and cheaper to reach for a handbook than to construct a finite element model from scratch.

LEARNING OUTCOMES

After you have studied Block 1, Part 4 you should be able to do the following:

4.1 Explain and use the principles of force equilibrium and strain compatibility for building mathematical models of engineering structures.

4.2 Analyse composite materials using a homogeneous strain (isostrain) or homogeneous stress (isostress) model, as appropriate.

4.3 Carry out simple design calculations for thin-walled cylindrical and spherical pressure vessels using a two-dimensional plane-stress model.

4.4 Perform simple calculations related to and describing the underlying mathematical principles of the finite element method.

4.5 Apply standard textbook solutions to derive stresses for given problems, without the need for deriving from first principles.

ANSWERS TO EXERCISES

EXERCISE 4.1

The component volume fractions for the glass and epoxy are:

$$\left(V_f\right)_g = 0.65$$
$$\left(V_f\right)_e = 1 - \left(V_f\right)_g = 0.35$$

Hence, parallel to the fibres, using Equation (4.3):

$$E = \left(V_f\right)_e E_e + \left(V_f\right)_g E_g$$
$$= \left(0.35 \times 3.5\right) \text{GPa} + \left(0.65 \times 72\right) \text{GPa}$$
$$= 48 \text{ GPa}$$

Note that the composite modulus is higher than that of the matrix and lower than that of the fibres, as might have been expected.

EXERCISE 4.2

Perpendicular to the fibres:

$$\frac{1}{E} = \frac{\left(V_f\right)_e}{E_e} + \frac{\left(V_f\right)_g}{E_g}$$
$$= \frac{0.35}{3.5 \text{ GPa}} + \frac{0.65}{72 \text{ GPa}}$$
$$= 0.109 \text{ GPa}^{-1}$$
$$E = 9.2 \text{ GPa}$$

EXERCISE 4.3

The maximum allowable stress in the sphere wall is 400 MPa; hence, rearranging Equation (4.6):

$$p = \frac{2 t_s \sigma_s}{r}$$
$$= \frac{2 \times 35 \times 10^{-3} \text{ m} \times 400 \times 10^6 \text{ Pa}}{17 \text{ m}}$$
$$= 1.6 \text{ MPa}$$

EXERCISE 4.4

(a) Axial strain:

$$\varepsilon_a = \frac{pr}{2t_c E}(1 - 2v)$$

$$= \frac{1 \times 10^6\,\text{Pa} \times 0.5\,\text{m}}{2 \times 0.01\,\text{m} \times 200 \times 10^9\,\text{Pa}}(1 - 2 \times 0.3)$$

$$= 1.25 \times 10^{-4} \times 0.4$$

$$= 5.00 \times 10^{-5}$$

Hoop strain:

$$\varepsilon_h = \frac{pr}{2t_c E}(2 - v) = 1.25 \times 10^{-4} \times 1.7 = 2.13 \times 10^{-4}$$

(b) In a spherical vessel the strain is the same in all directions:

$$\varepsilon_s = \frac{pr}{2t_s E}(1 - v) = 1.25 \times 10^{-4} \times 0.7 = 8.75 \times 10^{-5}$$

EXERCISE 4.5

(a) $3 \begin{Bmatrix} 9 \\ 12 \\ 6 \end{Bmatrix} = \begin{Bmatrix} 27 \\ 36 \\ 18 \end{Bmatrix}$

(b) $\dfrac{1}{3} \begin{bmatrix} 9 & 3 & 0 \\ 3 & 12 & 3 \\ 0 & 3 & 6 \end{bmatrix} = \begin{bmatrix} 3 & 1 & 0 \\ 1 & 4 & 1 \\ 0 & 1 & 2 \end{bmatrix}$

(c) $\dfrac{1}{3} \begin{Bmatrix} 0.009 \\ 0.012 \\ 0.006 \end{Bmatrix} \times 10^3 = \begin{Bmatrix} 0.003 \\ 0.004 \\ 0.002 \end{Bmatrix} \times 10^3 = \begin{Bmatrix} 3 \\ 4 \\ 2 \end{Bmatrix}$

(d) $\begin{bmatrix} 2 & 1 \\ 3 & 10 \end{bmatrix} \begin{Bmatrix} 5 \\ 4 \end{Bmatrix} = \begin{Bmatrix} (2 \times 5) + (1 \times 4) \\ (3 \times 5) + (10 \times 4) \end{Bmatrix} = \begin{Bmatrix} 10 + 4 \\ 15 + 40 \end{Bmatrix} = \begin{Bmatrix} 14 \\ 55 \end{Bmatrix}$

(e) $\begin{bmatrix} 1 & -1 \\ -1 & 1 \end{bmatrix} \begin{Bmatrix} 5 \\ 4 \end{Bmatrix} = \begin{Bmatrix} (1 \times 5) + (-1 \times 4) \\ (-1 \times 5) + (1 \times 4) \end{Bmatrix} = \begin{Bmatrix} 5 - 4 \\ -5 + 4 \end{Bmatrix} = \begin{Bmatrix} 1 \\ -1 \end{Bmatrix}$

(f) $\begin{bmatrix} 6 & -6 & 0 \\ -6 & 9 & -3 \\ 0 & -3 & 3 \end{bmatrix} \begin{Bmatrix} 1 \\ 0 \\ 1 \end{Bmatrix} = \begin{Bmatrix} (6 \times 1) + (-6 \times 0) + (0 \times 1) \\ (-6 \times 1) + (9 \times 0) + (-3 \times 1) \\ (0 \times 1) + (-3 \times 0) + (3 \times 1) \end{Bmatrix} = \begin{Bmatrix} 6 + 0 + 0 \\ -6 + 0 - 3 \\ 0 + 0 + 3 \end{Bmatrix} = \begin{Bmatrix} 6 \\ -9 \\ 3 \end{Bmatrix}$

EXERCISE 4.6

(a) The nodal forces when the nodal displacements are $u_1 = -0.1$ mm and $u_2 = 0.1$ mm are:

$$F_1 = \frac{AE}{L}(u_1 - u_2)$$

$$= \frac{10 \times 10^{-6} \text{ m}^2 \times 300 \times 10^9 \text{ N m}^{-2}}{300 \times 10^{-3} \text{ m}} \times (-0.1 - 0.1) \times 10^{-3} \text{ m}$$

$$= 1 \times 10^7 \text{ N m}^{-1} \times (-0.2) \times 10^{-3} \text{ m}$$

$$= -2 \text{ kN}$$

and

$$F_2 = \frac{AE}{L}(-u_1 + u_2) = 1 \times 10^7 \text{ N m}^{-1} \times (0.1 + 0.1) \times 10^{-3} \text{ m} = 2 \text{ kN}$$

$F_1 = -2$ kN acts in the negative x-direction and $F_2 = 2$ kN acts in the positive x-direction; the bar is in tension.

(b) The nodal forces for the nodal displacements $u_1 = 0.1$ mm and $u_2 = -0.1$ mm are:

$$F_1 = \frac{AE}{L}(u_1 - u_2) = 1 \times 10^7 \text{ N m}^{-1} \times (0.1 + 0.1) \times 10^{-3} \text{ m} = 2 \text{ kN}$$

and

$$F_2 = \frac{AE}{L}(-u_1 + u_2) = 1 \times 10^7 \text{ N m}^{-1} \times (-0.1 - 0.1) \times 10^{-3} \text{ m} = -2 \text{ kN}$$

$F_1 = 2$ kN acts in the positive x-direction and $F_2 = -2$ kN acts in the negative x-direction; the bar is in compression.

(c) The nodal forces for the nodal displacements $u_1 = 0.1$ mm and $u_2 = 0.1$ mm are:

$$F_1 = \frac{AE}{L}(u_1 - u_2) = 1 \times 10^7 \text{ N m}^{-1} \times (0.1 - 0.1) \times 10^{-3} \text{ m} = 0 \text{ N}$$

and

$$F_2 = \frac{AE}{L}(-u_1 + u_2) = 1 \times 10^7 \text{ N m}^{-1} \times (-0.1 + 0.1) \times 10^{-3} \text{ m} = 0 \text{ N}$$

There is no net force on the bar, even though the nodes are being displaced; therefore, it must be moving! When an object is displaced in this way, without it being deformed, it is said to undergo *rigid body displacement*. Finite element analysis needs to distinguish between deformation displacements, which are associated with net forces and stresses, and rigid body displacements, which are not.

EXERCISE 4.7

(a) Multiplying the matrix and vector:

$$\begin{bmatrix} 1 & -1 \\ -1 & 1 \end{bmatrix} \begin{Bmatrix} u_1 \\ u_2 \end{Bmatrix} = \begin{Bmatrix} (1 \times u_1) + (-1 \times u_2) \\ (-1 \times u_1) + (1 \times u_2) \end{Bmatrix} = \begin{Bmatrix} u_1 - u_2 \\ -u_1 + u_2 \end{Bmatrix}$$

(b) Equation (4.15) becomes:

$$\begin{Bmatrix} F_1 \\ F_2 \end{Bmatrix} = \frac{AE}{L} \begin{Bmatrix} u_1 - u_2 \\ -u_1 + u_2 \end{Bmatrix} = \begin{Bmatrix} \dfrac{AE}{L}(u_1 - u_2) \\ \dfrac{AE}{L}(-u_1 + u_2) \end{Bmatrix}$$

(c) By inspection, the two components of the column vector can be written as:

$$F_1 = \frac{AE}{L}(u_1 - u_2) \text{ and } F_2 = \frac{AE}{L}(-u_1 + u_2)$$

which are identical to Equations (4.13) and (4.14).

EXERCISE 4.8

(a) Multiplying the matrix Equation (4.19)

$$\begin{Bmatrix} F_1 \\ 0 \\ 100 \end{Bmatrix} \times 10^{-7} = \begin{bmatrix} 8 & -8 & 0 \\ -8 & 12 & -4 \\ 0 & -4 & 4 \end{bmatrix} \begin{Bmatrix} 0 \\ u_2 \\ u_3 \end{Bmatrix} = \begin{Bmatrix} 0 - 8u_2 + 0 \\ 0 + 12u_2 - 4u_3 \\ 0 - 4u_2 + 4u_3 \end{Bmatrix}$$

which represents the equations:

$$F_1 \times 10^{-7} = -8u_2 \qquad\qquad (4.20)$$

$$0 = 12u_2 - 4u_3 \qquad\qquad (4.21)$$

$$100 \times 10^{-7} = -4u_2 + 4u_3 \qquad\qquad (4.22)$$

(b) Adding Equations (4.21) and (4.22) gives:

$$100 \times 10^{-7} = 8u_2$$

and rearranging

$$u_2 = \frac{100 \times 10^{-7}}{8} = 1.25 \times 10^{-6} \text{ m}$$

From Equation (4.21):

$$4u_3 = 12u_2$$

$$u_3 = \frac{12}{4}u_2$$

$$= \frac{12}{4} \times 1.25 \times 10^{-6}$$

$$= 3.75 \times 10^{-6} \text{ m}$$

(c) Substituting u_1 into Equation (4.20):

$$F_1 \times 10^{-7} = -8 \times 1.25 \times 10^{-6}$$

and rearranging

$$F_1 = \frac{-8 \times 1.25 \times 10^{-6}}{10^{-7}} = -100 \text{ N}$$

Note that this reaction force balances the force applied at node 3, as expected.

ANSWERS TO SELF-ASSESSMENT QUESTIONS

SAQ 4.1

(a) First determine the volume fractions of the components, identical to the area fractions:

$$(V_f)_s = \frac{10 \times 500 \times 10^{-6} \text{ m}^2}{0.25 \text{ m}^2} = 0.02 \text{ and } (V_f)_c = 1 - (V_f)_c = 0.98$$

and then the composite modulus is:

$$E = (V_f)_c E_c + (V_f)_s E_s = (0.98 \times 50) \text{ GPa} + (0.02 \times 200) \text{ GPa} = 53 \text{ GPa}$$

(b) The applied stress is $\sigma = 2000 \times 10^3 \text{ N}/0.25 \text{ m}^2 = 8.0 \text{ MPa}$, so the strain in the column can be deduced from Hooke's law using the composite modulus derived in part (a):

$$\varepsilon = \frac{\sigma}{E} = \frac{8.0 \times 10^6 \text{ Pa}}{53 \times 10^9 \text{ Pa}} = 1.51 \times 10^{-4}$$

(c) Assuming strain compatibility $\varepsilon = \varepsilon_c = \varepsilon_s$ and so the average stress in the steel is:

$$\sigma_s = \varepsilon E_s = 1.5 \times 10^{-4} \times 200 \times 10^9 \text{ Pa} = 30 \text{ MPa}$$

and in the concrete:

$$\sigma_c = \varepsilon E_c = 1.5 \times 10^{-4} \times 50 \times 10^9 \text{ Pa} = 7.5 \text{ MPa}$$

(d) From the right-hand side of Equation (4.1):

$$(V_f)_c \sigma_c + (V_f)_s \sigma_s = (0.98 \times 7.5) \text{ MPa} + (0.02 \times 30) \text{ MPa}$$
$$= 8.0 \text{ MPa}$$

which is equal to the applied stress.

SAQ 4.2

(a) The cross-sectional area fraction (and hence volume fraction) is simply proportional to the thickness ratio, hence:

$$(V_f)_{Al} = \frac{1.4 \text{ mm}}{2.0 \text{ mm}} = 0.7 \text{ and } (V_f)_{ss} = 0.3$$

So, parallel to the layers, using Equation (4.3):

$$E = (V_f)_{Al} E_{Al} + (V_f)_{ss} E_{ss}$$
$$= (0.7 \times 70) \text{ GPa} + (0.3 \times 190) \text{ GPa}$$
$$= 106 \text{ GPa}$$

and, perpendicular to the layers, using Equation (4.5):

$$\frac{1}{E} = \frac{\left(V_f\right)_{Al}}{E_{Al}} + \frac{\left(V_f\right)_{ss}}{E_{ss}}$$

$$= \frac{0.7}{70 \text{ GPa}} + \frac{0.3}{190 \text{ GPa}}$$

$$= 0.0116 \text{ GPa}^{-1}$$

$$E = 86 \text{ GPa}$$

(b) Parallel to the layers:

$$k = \left(V_f\right)_{Al} k_{Al} + \left(V_f\right)_{ss} k_{ss}$$

$$= \left(0.7 \times 210\right) \text{ W m}^{-1} \, {}^{\circ}\text{C}^{-1} + \left(0.3 \times 15\right) \text{ W m}^{-1} \, {}^{\circ}\text{C}^{-1}$$

$$= 152 \text{ W m}^{-1} \, {}^{\circ}\text{C}^{-1}$$

Perpendicular to the layers:

$$\frac{1}{k} = \frac{\left(V_f\right)_{Al}}{k_{Al}} + \frac{\left(V_f\right)_{ss}}{k_{ss}} = \frac{0.7}{210} + \frac{0.3}{15} = 0.0233 \text{ W}^{-1} \text{ m } {}^{\circ}\text{C}$$

$$k = 43 \text{ W m}^{-1} \, {}^{\circ}\text{C}^{-1}$$

(c) For compatibility $\varepsilon = \varepsilon_{Al} = \varepsilon_{ss}$ and applying Hooke's law to the aluminium layer, the strain is:

$$\varepsilon = \frac{\sigma_{Al}}{E_{Al}} = \frac{50 \times 10^6 \text{ Pa}}{70 \times 10^9 \text{ Pa}} = 7.14 \times 10^{-4}$$

Again, using Hooke's law, the average stress in the stainless steel is:

$$\sigma_{ss} = \varepsilon E_{ss} = 7.14 \times 10^{-4} \times 190 \times 10^9 \text{ Pa} = 136 \text{ MPa}$$

SAQ 4.3

(a) For loading parallel to the wood layers, a homogeneous strain model is suitable; for loading perpendicular to the wood layers, a homogeneous stress model can be used.

(b) Assuming that the concrete contains a well-distributed mix of randomly oriented particles, then the homogenous stress model can be applied in any direction.

(c) For loading parallel to the fibres, a homogeneous strain model is suitable; for loading perpendicular to the fibres, a homogeneous stress model can be used.

(d) The homogeneous stress model can be applied in any direction parallel to the plane in which the fibres are randomly oriented, and also in a direction perpendicular to the layering.

(e) Since the particles, being spheres, have no effective alignment, then the homogeneous stress model can be applied in any direction.

SAQ 4.4

(a) If the internal pressure is 1% of the shell stress, then from Equation (4.6):

$$\frac{p}{\sigma_s} = \frac{2t_s}{r} = \frac{1}{100}$$

Hence:

$$t_s = \frac{r}{2 \times 100} = \frac{5\ m}{200} = 25 \times 10^{-3}\ m$$

The required wall thickness is 25 mm.

(b) For large quantities of liquid, the extra pressure caused by the weight of the fluid becomes an issue. This varies with depth, so the internal pressure on the vessel walls is no longer strictly uniform.

(c) The extra pressure caused by a column of fluid 10 m high is:

$$\rho g h = (550 \times 9.8 \times 10)\ Pa = 0.054\ MPa$$

which is more than an order of magnitude below the design pressure for the vessel we have been considering. Hence, the analysis we have used presents a reasonable approximation.

SAQ 4.5

(a) Axial stress:

$$\sigma_a = \frac{pr}{2t_c} = \frac{1 \times 10^6\ Pa \times 0.5\ m}{2 \times 0.01\ m} = 25\ MPa$$

Hoop stress:

$$\sigma_h = \frac{pr}{t_c} = 50\ MPa$$

(b) Mohr's circle is drawn in Figure 4.20 using σ_h and σ_a as principal stresses. The maximum shear stress in the surface is:

$$\tau_{max} = (\sigma_h - \sigma_a)/2 = 12.5\ MPa$$

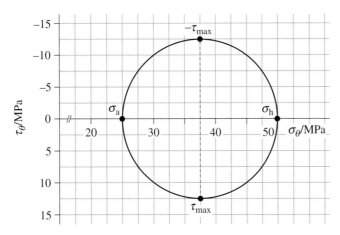

Figure 4.20 Mohr's circle for the cylindrical vessel

Note that both σ_h and σ_a are tensile, so the minimum principal stress must be zero, assuming plane stress.

SAQ 4.6

To maintain compatibility:

$$\frac{t_c}{t_s} = \frac{2-v}{1-v} = \frac{1.7}{0.7} = 2.43$$

So the 'sphere' thickness of the ends must be:

$$t_s = \frac{t_c}{2.43} = \frac{1\,\text{cm}}{2.43} = 0.41\,\text{cm}$$

.

SAQ 4.7

(a) For fracture, it is the maximum tensile stress that is important, and that is the hoop stress. Applying a safety factor of 2 to the tensile fracture strength of the alloy, σ_h should not be allowed to exceed 160 MPa. Hence, rearranging Equation (4.8), the minimum wall thickness should be:

$$
\begin{aligned}
t_c &= \frac{pr}{\sigma_h} \\
&= \frac{300 \times 10^3\ \text{Pa} \times 0.033\ \text{m}}{160 \times 10^6\ \text{Pa}} \\
&= 6.2 \times 10^{-5}\ \text{m} \\
&= 0.062\ \text{mm}
\end{aligned}
$$

(b) The Tresca yield criterion is:

$$\sigma_{\text{yield}} = \sigma_1 - \sigma_3$$

The axial and hoop stresses are principal stresses. They are both tensile (positive), and so, for plane stress, the minimum principal stress σ_3 is zero. The maximum principal stress is σ_h. Hence, the Tresca criterion becomes:

$$\sigma_{\text{yield}} = \sigma_1 - \sigma_3 = \sigma_h - 0 = \sigma_h$$

that is, yield occurs when the hoop stress is equal to the uniaxial yield stress. Again, applying a safety factor of 2 to the uniaxial yield stress means that σ_h should not exceed 125 MPa, and the necessary wall thickness is:

$$
\begin{aligned}
t_c &= \frac{pr}{\sigma_h} \\
&= \frac{300 \times 10^3\ \text{Pa} \times 0.033\ \text{m}}{125 \times 10^6\ \text{Pa}} \\
&= 7.9 \times 10^{-5}\ \text{m} \\
&= 0.079\ \text{mm}
\end{aligned}
$$

Most modern drinks cans do indeed have a remarkably small wall thickness of ~0.1 mm.

SAQ 4.8

(a) The elemental strain $\varepsilon^{(1)}$ in the positive x-direction is:

$$\varepsilon^{(1)} = \frac{-u_1 + u_2}{L^{(1)}} = \frac{1.25 \times 10^{-6} \text{ m}}{50 \times 10^{-3} \text{ m}} = 2.5 \times 10^{-5}$$

The elemental strain $\varepsilon^{(2)}$ in the positive x-direction is:

$$\varepsilon^{(2)} = \frac{-u_2 + u_3}{L^{(2)}} = \frac{\left(-1.25 \times 10^{-6} + 3.75 \times 10^{-6}\right) \text{m}}{50 \times 10^{-3} \text{ m}} = 5.0 \times 10^{-5}$$

(b) The elemental stresses are given by:

$$\sigma^{(1)} = E^{(1)}\varepsilon^{(1)} = 200 \times 10^9 \text{ Pa} \times 2.50 \times 10^{-5} = 5.0 \text{ MPa}$$

and

$$\sigma^{(2)} = E^{(2)}\varepsilon^{(2)} = 200 \times 10^9 \text{ Pa} \times 5.0 \times 10^{-5} = 10.0 \text{ MPa}$$

(c) The theoretical stress for area 1 is:

$$\frac{\text{force}}{A^{(1)}} = \frac{100 \text{ N}}{20 \times 10^{-6} \text{ m}^2} = 5 \text{ MPa}$$

and for area 2:

$$\frac{\text{force}}{A^{(2)}} = \frac{100 \text{ N}}{10 \times 10^{-6} \text{ m}^2} = 10 \text{ MPa}$$

SAQ 4.9

Since the bar is 1 mm thick, for the given cross-sectional areas, it must have width of $w = 20$ mm and $h = 10$ mm either side of the step; hence $w/h = 2$.

The fillet radius is $r = 1$ mm, so reading from the $w/h = 2$ line on Figure 4.19 at the point where $r/h = 0.1$ indicates that K_t lies somewhere between 2.4 and 2.5. The higher value represents a wise conservative choice for component design.

The stress concentration factor is defined as:

$$K_t = \frac{\sigma_{\text{max}}}{\sigma_{\text{nominal}}}$$

and the nominal stress across the bar where it has the smallest cross-sectional area is 10 MPa, so:

$$\sigma_{\text{max}} = K_t\sigma_{\text{nominal}} = 2.5 \times 10 \text{ MPa} = 25 \text{ MPa}$$

ACKNOWLEDGEMENTS

Grateful acknowledgement is made to the following sources:

FIGURES

Figure 4.3(a): © Eye of Science/Science Photo Library.

Figure 4.3(b): From www.metallographic.com, Pace Technologies.

Figure 4.3(c): © Phil Degginger/Alamy.

Figure 4.3(d): From Stock.Xchng, Dave Gostisha.

Figure 4.3(e): Courtesy of SCPS Group, France.

Figure 4.5: Courtesy of University of Goettingen.

Figure 4.7 (above): Hendrickson International.

Figure 4.7 (below): Courtesy of All-Clad UK.

Figure 4.10(a), © Paul Rapson/Science Photo Library.

Figure 4.10(b): Courtesy of Pt. Meco Inoxprima.

Figure 4.10(c): © Martyn F. Chillmaid/Science Photo Library.

Figure 4.10(d): Courtesy of Avelair.

Figure 4.10(e): © Martin Bond/Science Photo Library.

Figure 4.10(f): © Sinclair Stammers/Science Photo Library.

Figure 4.12: NKK Corporation, JFE Holdings, Japan.

Figure 4.14: © Michael R.G. Hughes/StockXchng, www.fiveacesdesign.com

Every effort has been made to contact copyright holders. If any have been inadvertently overlooked the publishers will be pleased to make the necessary arrangements at the first opportunity.

COURSE TEAM ACKNOWLEDGEMENTS

This part was prepared for the course team by Martin Rist.

T357 COURSE TEAM

Professor Michael Fitzpatrick (course team chair)

Andy Harding (course manager)

Jackie Burnicle (course manager)

ACADEMIC STAFF

Dr Alun Armstrong

Professor Adrian Demaid

Professor Chris Earl

Professor Lyndon Edwards

Dr Salih Gungor

Michael Hush

Dr Peter Lewis

Dr Jim Moffatt

Dr Ed Murphy

Dr Martin Rist

EXTERNAL ASSESSOR

Professor Lindsay Greer, University of Cambridge

SUPPORT STAFF

Debbie Derbyshire (course team secretary)

Colin Gagg

Stan Hiller

Gordon Imlach

Pete Ledgard

Rehana Malik

PRODUCTION TEAM

Kirsten Barnett

Annette Booz

Philippa Broadbent

Lisa Carrick

Teresa Cox

Sarah Crompton

Daphne Cross

Anna Edgley-Smith

Vicky Eves

Chris French

Carol Houghton

Jonathan Martyn

Katie Meade

Lara Mynors

Deana Plummer

Lynn Short

Susanne Umerski